34

ool

'3

34

CARAVANS

Senior Author
William K. Durr

Senior Coordinating Author
John J. Pikulski

Coordinating Authors
Rita M. Bean
J. David Cooper
Nicholas A. Glaser
M. Jean Greenlaw
Hugh Schoephoerster

Authors
Mary Lou Alsin
Kathryn Au
Rosalinda B. Barrera
Joseph E. Brzeinski
Ruth P. Bunyan

Jacqueline C. Comas
Frank X. Estrada
Robert L. Hillerich
Timothy G. Johnson
Pamela A. Mason
Joseph S. Renzulli

HOUGHTON MIFFLIN COMPANY   **BOSTON**

Atlanta   Dallas   Geneva, Illinois   Palo Alto   Princeton   Toronto

Acknowledgments

For each of the selections listed below, grateful acknowledgment is made for permission to adapt and/or reprint original or copyrighted material, as follows:

"Benny's Flag," adapted from *Benny's Flag,* by Phyllis Krasilovsky. Copyright © 1960 by Phyllis Krasilovsky and reprinted by permission of the author. Originally published by The World Publishing Company.

"Blue-Wings-Flying," adapted from *Blue-Wings-Flying,* by Elizabeth Willis DeHuff. Copyright © 1977 by Elizabeth Willis DeHuff. Reprinted by permission of Frances D. Barry.

"Butterfly, butterfly," from Bulletins of the Bureau of American Ethnology, Bulletin number 165, *Music of Acoma, Isleta, Cochiti, and Zuni Pueblos* by Frances Densmore, 1957. Smithsonian Institution, Washington, D.C. Reprinted by permission of Smithsonian Institution Press.

"Digging Up Dinosaurs," adapted from *Digging Up Dinosaurs,* by Aliki (Thomas Y. Crowell). Copyright © 1981 by Aliki Brandenberg. Adapted and reprinted by permission of Harper & Row, Publishers, Inc. and The Bodley Head, Ltd.

"Dragon Stew," adapted from *Dragon Stew,* by Tom McGowen. Copyright © 1969 by Tom McGowen. Reprinted by permission of the author.

Continued on page 398.

Printed in the U.S.A.
ISBN: 0-395-43683-4

CDEFGHIJ-D-943210/89

Contents

Magazine One

Caravans
Magazine One

Contents

The
Green Thumb Thief

by Mary Blount Christian

Plants in the neighborhood are beginning to
mysteriously disappear. Will Deke and Snitch,
who have their own detective agency, be able
to catch the Green Thumb Thief?

I opened the newspaper and found our ad.

MYSTERIES SOLVED

A DOLLAR A DAY

DEKE KING AND FRIEND
THE UNDERCOVER KIDS

My friend Snitch said, "I hope it gets us some business. We spent all our money on this ad." He pulled his ear. Snitch always pulls his ear when he's upset.

The phone rang. I answered. It was the first call on our ad. A woman said her name was Flora Greene. She told me she needed help right away.

Snitch and I rode our bikes straight to her house. The yard was filled with bushes and plants. It looked like a forest. Flora Greene asked us inside. Behind her a small piece of fluff jumped about. "Is that a dog?" I asked, making a guess.

"Of course," she said. "That's Hercules." At the sound of its name, the fluff wiggled. I reached over to pat it.

Flora Greene took us through the house to the back yard. She had a greenhouse there full of plants and flowers.

"I need you to take care of these while I'm away on a trip," she said, "and Hercules, too."

Snitch pulled on his ear.

"But we are detectives, not babysitters," I explained. "We're the Undercover Kids, and we solve mysteries."

"I want to *stop* a mystery before it happens," she said, pushing a newspaper toward me. She'd circled a headline in red.

COSTLY PLANTS TAKEN
GREEN THUMB THIEF AT LARGE
POLICE STUMPED, FIND NO CLUES

The paper said there was one suspect — a plant shop owner at the flea market. None of the stolen plants could be identified, so the police had to let the shop owner go. Without positive identification, they had no proof that he was the thief.

"I will pay you twice what you usually get," Flora Greene said.

I looked at Snitch, and he nodded happily. I shrugged and then said, "I suppose we can think of ourselves as bodyguards."

I took out my notebook and asked, "What do you want us to do?"

She touched a floppy-looking plant. "First you'll have to get to know my plants. This is Emily. Say hello to Emily."

I was a little startled that the plants had names but took notes on them anyway.

Flora Greene went on to say, "Plants need to be talked to. They can tell if you don't like them."

I nodded. It would be embarrassing to talk to plants, but I thought about all of the money we'd make.

"Do they all eat at the same time?" I asked.

"Oh my, no! Emily is always thirsty and needs water every day. But Samantha, here, takes water just once a week."

I wrote down information about Hercules, too.

On the way home, I told Snitch, "We'll never remember how often each plant gets water. We'll need a reminder."

"Reminder?" Snitch asked.

He thought a moment and then said, "You know how you sometimes tie a piece of string around your finger to remember something?"

I had a feeling he was on to something. "Go on," I said.

"Well, maybe we could tie yarn on the plants," Snitch said. "We could use different colors."

"Oh, do you mean we could have a code?" I asked. "Different colors of yarn would let us know to water plants on different days?"

Snitch nodded. I could tell he was pleased with himself.

The next day Snitch and I took pieces of colored yarn to Flora Greene's house. We put red yarn on the plants that needed water every day, blue yarn on the ones that needed water every other day, and green yarn on the ones that needed water just once a week.

"I'll water the plants," I told Snitch. "You and Hercules stand guard in the front yard." I knew we had to be careful with the Green Thumb Thief around.

Soon Snitch and Hercules came back inside.

I looked at Hercules. "How did he get so dirty?" I asked Snitch.

"He fell in the hole out front," Snitch answered.

"There isn't any hole out front," I said. "Or I know there wasn't one when we got here."

"There is now," Snitch answered.

I went outside to check. Sure enough, there was a hole where a big plant used to be. Someone must have stolen it while we were busy putting yarn on the plants inside.

"The Green Thumb Thief has taken more plants right under the noses of the Undercover Kids," I said. "We have got to find that thief!"

"What do we do now?" asked Snitch.

"I think it's time to go undercover," I decided. "Put on a disguise and meet me back here. Make sure that your disguise has something to do with gardens!" I said, jumping on my bike.

I searched my bedroom and found the perfect disguise. It was a good thing I had played a tree in the school play. Who would suspect a tree?

I hurried back to Flora Greene's. I decided to guard the front yard — there were still some nice plants left. I kept watch through my disguise and waited for Snitch. When I saw him, I couldn't believe my eyes. He was riding down the street dressed like a chicken!

"Why a chicken?" I yelled. "I tell you to disguise yourself for the garden and you dress up like a chicken?"

"I couldn't find any other disguise." He shrugged. "Anyway, chickens get into gardens."

Snitch kneeled down on the ground. Pretty soon we heard a noise coming from the back yard.

"Is that Hercules?" I asked.

Snitch looked at me and then said, "It sounds as if something's wrong."

We ran to the back of the house. The greenhouse door was open. Emily was missing, and so was Samantha. Several other plants were gone, too.

Hercules came out from behind a big plant. He was shaking all over. A piece of cloth was hanging from his front tooth.

"Good dog, Hercules," I said. "I think that piece of cloth belongs to the thief." Hercules wiggled.

I put the cloth into my pocket. Snitch picked up Hercules, and we looked for more clues.

There were tire tracks in the driveway, but they disappeared a block away.

"What would a thief do with all those plants?" Snitch asked.

"Sell them?" I said.

"There's a shop at the flea market that sells plants," Snitch said. "The newspaper story said that the owner was under suspicion, but nobody could positively identify their plants."

We went to the flea market. There were plants everywhere, but they all looked alike. Then I saw a floppy-looking plant that I thought I had seen before.

"Go and find a police officer ... and *hurry!*" I whispered to Snitch. "Take a look over there. That's Emily!"

As I went over to take a closer look at Emily, a big man came up to me. He stared down at me. "Hey," he said. "Get lost, tree, before I turn you into toothpicks."

By that time, Snitch had found a police officer. He brought her over. She smiled at me. "I hear that you've identified one of your stolen plants," she said. "How are you able to tell which plant is yours?"

I pointed to Emily's red yarn and to the drawing I'd made of her in my notebook. "This is Emily," I said. "We put red yarn on her so that we could remember to water her every day."

"He must have planted the evidence," the man said in a mean voice.

"*Planted?*" the officer said. "Are you trying to be funny?" She turned to me. "That's not bad proof. But if this man said he bought the plants from someone else, we'll need more evidence."

Hercules barked. I remembered the cloth I'd found in his mouth and showed it to the police officer.

The plant shop owner smiled when he saw the cloth.

"He's changed clothes," Snitch whispered to me. "We can't prove a thing."

"Let's find out how good a detective your little friend is," the police officer said. She held the piece of cloth in front of Hercules' nose. His nose wrinkled. The plant shop owner backed away.

Suddenly Hercules began to run around the plants. He sniffed all around them. He pulled at a pair of pants that had been thrown behind some flower pots.

The officer held them up. There was a hole in them. The piece of cloth fit the hole perfectly, and pieces of Hercules' fur were on the pants. "Shedding is Hercules' best trick," I said.

A reporter came to the flea market. He took a picture of Snitch, Hercules, and me with Emily.

The officer took the Green Thumb Thief down to the station. Then she came back and helped us get Emily and the other plants back to the greenhouse.

When Flora Greene got home from her trip, she saw the picture of us in the newspaper. She paid us *three* times what we usually get and said we were worth it.

It wasn't a bad day's work for a dog, a tree, and a big chicken!

Author

Mary Blount Christian is well known for her entertaining mysteries for young readers. Her three children have given her ideas for the more than thirty children's books she has written. In her home state of Texas, she created a weekly educational TV show on children's books that has been shown nationwide.

Selection Wrap-up

Summary Questions

Deke and Snitch were detectives. Use these questions to tell about their first case.

1. What were the boys supposed to do on their first case?
2. How did the boys catch the Green Thumb Thief? What clues helped them?
3. Do you think the boys were smart detectives? Why or why not?
4. Pretend you are Snitch. Tell about your favorite part of the case.

The Reading and Writing Connection

Read these newspaper headlines about the mystery of the Green Thumb Thief.

Choose one headline and write a newspaper report. Give all the important information from the story to tell about the headline. Try to use some words from the box.

mysteriously	**suspect**	**identification**
suspicion	**evidence**	**embarrassing**
prove	**officer**	

The White Stallion

by Elizabeth Shub

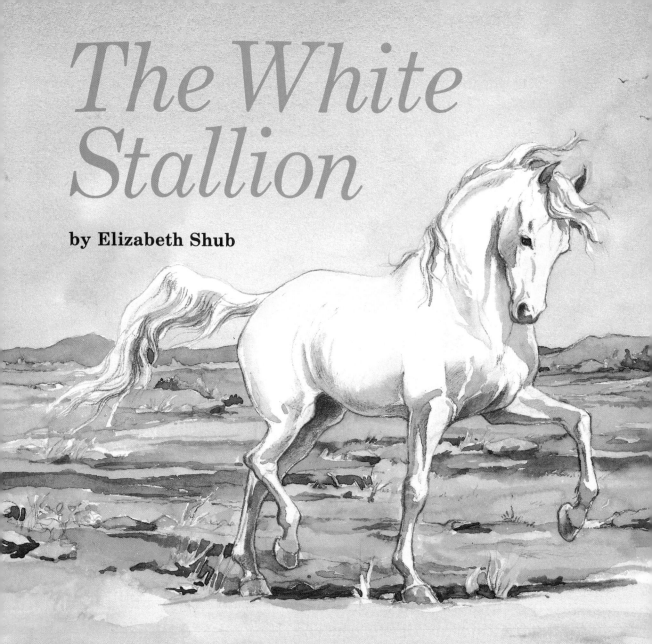

Long ago, a girl named Gretchen was on a
horse that strayed from the wagon train.
When Gretchen became surrounded by a herd
of wild horses, would the white stallion
be able to rescue her?

This is a story that has been told in Gretchen's family for many, many years. It is about an adventure Gretchen's great-great-grandmother was believed to have had when she was a girl about Gretchen's age. Gretchen's mother is telling the story to Gretchen.

It was 1845. Three families were on their way West. They planned to settle there. They traveled in covered wagons. Each wagon was drawn by four horses. These wagons were called Conestoga wagons.

Gretchen and her family were in the last wagon. Mother and Father sat on the driver's seat. The children were inside with the household goods. Bedding, blankets, pots and pans, a table, chairs, and a dresser took up most of the space.

There was not much room left for Trudy, John, Billy, and Gretchen. Gretchen was the youngest.

Behind the wagon walked Anna, the family's old mare. She was not tied to the wagon but followed faithfully. She carried two sacks of cornmeal on her back.

It was hot in the afternoon sun, and the children were too warm. The wagon cover shaded them, but little air came in through the openings at the front and back.

John kicked Billy. Billy pushed him, and he bumped Gretchen. Trudy, the oldest, who was trying to read, asked them to be good. Their quarrel was stopped by Father's voice.

"Quick, everybody! Look at the mustangs."

The children rushed to the back of the wagon. In the distance, they could see the wild horses. The horses galloped away and, in minutes, were out of sight.

"Look at Anna," John said.

The old mare stood still. She had turned her head toward the mustangs. Her usually floppy ears were lifted high. The wagon had moved some distance before Anna trotted after it.

It was hotter than ever inside.

"Father," Gretchen called, "may I ride on Anna for a while?"

Father stopped the wagon and came to the back. He lifted Gretchen onto the mare. The cornmeal sacks made a nice seat. He tied her onto the mare carefully so that she would not fall off.

As the wagon train moved on, Gretchen fell asleep in the warmth of the sun. The wagon train was following a trail in Texas along the Guadalupe River. The back wheel of the first wagon hit a big rock, and a wheel broke off. The whole train stopped. Anna trotted away, with Gretchen sleeping on her back, and no one noticed.

The travelers decided to stay there for the night. Children gathered firewood and got water from the river. The grownups prepared food. It was not until the wheel had been fixed, and they were ready to eat, that Gretchen and Anna were missed.

The men tried to follow the mare's tracks but soon lost them. It was getting dark, and there was nothing to do but stay where they were. They would search again at the first sign of light. Faithful Anna, they thought, would return. She probably had found some grass to eat. She would come back when she had eaten all she wanted.

Gretchen awoke to the sound of lapping. Anna was drinking noisily from a stream. A short distance away stood about ten wild horses. They were light brown with dark brown stripes down their backs or on their legs.

After Anna had finished drinking, she moved toward the mares. They trotted up to her as if to say hello. Then they crossed necks with Anna. They were so friendly that Gretchen was not afraid. She did not even know that Anna had trotted away from the wagon train.

Suddenly the horses began to nibble at the sacks on Anna's back. They had smelled the cornmeal. In their eagerness, they nipped Gretchen's legs. Frightened, Gretchen screamed and tried to get out of the way. She tried to loosen the ropes that held her, but she could not free herself.

Out of nowhere, there came a great white stallion. He pranced and whinnied. He swished his long white tail. He stood on his hind legs, his white mane flying.

The mares moved out of his way. The white stallion came up to Anna. He carefully bit through the ropes that tied Gretchen. Gently, he took hold of the back of her dress with his teeth and lifted her to the ground. He seemed to motion to the mares with his head, and then he galloped away.

The mares followed at once, and Anna followed them.

Gretchen was left alone. She did not know what to do. "Father will find me soon," she said out loud to make herself feel better. She was hungry, but there was nothing to eat. She walked to the stream to get a drink of water. Then she sat down on a rock to wait.

Gretchen waited and waited, but there was no sign of Father, and no sign of Anna. The sun went down. It began to get dark. "Anna!" Gretchen called. "Anna! Anna! Anna!" There was no answering sound.

Gretchen sat up frightened. She heard the sound of a coyote, but it sounded as if it were far away.

She heard the sound of leaves and the call of redbirds. Gretchen began to cry. She made a place for herself on some dry leaves next to a tree. She curled up against the tree and cried until she fell asleep.

Morning light woke Gretchen. The stream sparkled in the sunlight. Gretchen washed her face and took a drink of water from the clear stream. She looked for Anna. She called her name, but Anna did not come. Gretchen was so hungry that she tried to eat some grass, but it had a nasty taste. She sat on her rock near the stream.

She looked at the red spots on her legs where she had been nipped by the horses. Then she began to cry again. A rabbit came by. It looked at her in such a funny way that she stopped crying. She walked along the stream. She knew she must not go far. "If you are lost," Mother had warned, "stay where you are. That will make it easier to find you." Gretchen walked back to her rock.

It was afternoon when she heard the sound of a galloping horse. A moment later, Anna trotted up to the stream. The sacks of meal were gone. As the old mare took a drink of water, Gretchen hugged her and she patted her back. Anna would find her way back to the wagon train.

Gretchen tried to climb on Anna's back, but even without the sacks, the mare was too high. There was a fallen tree not far away. Gretchen thought she might be able to stand on it to climb onto the mare. She tugged at Anna, but Anna would not move. Gretchen pulled and pushed, but Anna wouldn't move.

Then she heard hoofbeats coming up behind her. Before she could turn around, she felt something pulling at the collar of her dress. It was the white stallion. Again he lifted Gretchen by the back of her dress and sat her on Anna's back. He nuzzled and pushed the old mare. Anna began to walk.

The white stallion walked close behind Anna for a moment. Then, as if to say good-by, he stood on his hind legs, whinnied, and galloped away.

Gretchen always believed that the white stallion had told Anna to take her back to the wagon train. For that is what Anna did.

Long ago, a proud white stallion roamed the plains of Texas. Cowboys said he was the greatest horse that ever lived. And Gretchen must have felt that the cowboys were right.

Author

Elizabeth Shub, who knows several languages, has translated and retold many old tales, among them *Clever Kate* from the Brothers Grimm. She worked with the prize-winning author Isaac Singer on many of his books. *The White Stallion* is an old Western legend that she has retold. It was chosen as a Notable Book of 1982 by the American Library Association.

Selection Wrap-up

Summary Questions

Gretchen got lost, but she ended up back at the wagon train. Use these questions to tell how.

1. How did Gretchen get lost? How did she get back?
2. Do you think the white stallion helped Gretchen? Why or why not?
3. Pretend you are Gretchen. Tell your family everything that happened after you got lost.

The Reading and Writing Connection

Gretchen saw a lot of horses. The chart below tells about some of the horses.

Horses	What They Did	Where
Anna wild mare white stallion	strayed galloped roamed	from the wagon by the stream the Texas plains

Imagine that you just saw one of these horses. Write a paragraph about the horse. Describe the horse. Then tell what it was doing and where you saw it. Also tell what you thought about it. Try to use some words from the box.

rescue	**motion**	**eagerness**
faithfully	**coyote**	**surrounded**

Likes and Opposites

The horse **strayed** from the wagon train.

The sentence above tells about, or describes, the picture. There is more than one way that you can tell what is happening in the picture.

This sentence uses another word in place of *strayed:*

The horse **wandered** from the wagon train.

The words *strayed* and *wandered* are similar in meaning.

Read these sentences:

1. Gretchen **pulled** at the horse's reins.
2. Her brothers and sisters will **fight** about whose turn it is to steer the wagon.
3. The mare **hurried** to the stream for a drink of water.

Now use one of the words below in place of each word in boldface type if it has a similar meaning:

quarrel   rushed   tugged

This horse is **wild.**

Sometimes words mean the opposite of each other. When things are opposite, they are as different as can be. Which word in the sentence below is the opposite of *wild?*

This horse is **tame.**

The words *tame* and *wild* are opposites.

Read these sentences:

1. Gretchen was the **youngest** child in her family.

2. The character in this story is very **kind.**
3. She was **ashamed** of her behavior.

Each sentence you just read has a boldface word. Use one of these words in its place if it has an opposite or nearly opposite meaning:

nasty   proud   oldest

Read these sentences:

1. The cornmeal sacks made a **nice** seat.
2. The **back** wheel of the first wagon hit a big rock.
3. Cowboys said the white stallion was the **greatest** horse that ever lived.

Read each sentence using a word that means *almost the same thing* as the word in boldface type. Then read the sentence again using a word that means the *opposite* of the word in boldface type.

Using Context

When you are reading, you may come to a word that you have never seen before. Even if you have no idea what it means, you may be able to learn something about its meaning by using the other words in the sentence. This is called **using the context**.

You must read and think about the other words in the sentence. These other words can give you a clue to the meaning of the word that you don't know. Read the sentence below that has the word *meadow* in it. What do the other words in this sentence tell you about the meaning of the word *meadow*?

We saw wildflowers and birds as we walked through the tall grass in the **meadow**.

By reading the other words in the sentence, you can tell that a *meadow* is a place where you can walk through tall grass and see wildflowers and birds. All of the context that gave the meaning of *meadow* in that sentence came *before* the word.

Now read the two sentences at the top of the next page. See where the context comes that helps with the meaning of the word *banister*.

He held on to the **banister.** He didn't want to fall as he walked down the stairs.

The context before the word *banister* tells you that it is something that could be held on to. But many things could be held. The context after the word *banister* gives you much more meaning for the word. Now you know that it is something to hold on to *and* that it will help keep you from falling as you walk down the stairs. A banister is the railing that goes along a set of stairs. The context that came *after* the word was more helpful than the context that came before it.

You can often learn something about the meaning of new words, such as *meadow* and *banister,* by using the context.

The context can be other words in the same sentence or it can be words in other sentences. The context that helps give meaning can come *before* or *after* the new word.

Sometimes the context that helps with the meaning of a word comes *before and after* the new word. Read the sentences below. See where the context comes that helps with the meaning of the word *sculpture*.

Tom carefully shaped the clay with his fingers. He hoped his **sculpture** would look like the rabbit he had seen in the back yard.

How were the words before and after *sculpture* helpful in learning about the meaning of the word?

Using Context to Get Word Meanings

As you read the following story, use the context to help you with the meaning of each boldface word:

It started out to be a very **pleasant** day. It was warm and sunny. Julie was sailing with Kate, her older sister. Kate was an **expert** with the boat. She had won many sailing races in the family's **sloop.**

Soon Julie **observed** the sky becoming darker and darker. Julie was afraid that the boat might **capsize** in the wind. Kate said, "Don't be scared, Julie. The boat won't turn over. Just **compose** yourself. We'll be home before the storm begins."

How was using the context helpful in getting the meaning of the words in boldface type? What other words in the story helped you get the meaning? Was the helpful context before, after, or before and after?

Skill Summary

- Using the other words as clues to the meaning of a word as you read is called *using the context*.
- Context can help you learn something about the meaning of a word that you have never seen before.
- The context that helps you with the meaning may come before the word, after the word, or both before and after the word.

Through Grandpa's Eyes

by Patricia MacLachlan

John enjoys spending time with his Grandpa, who is blind. How is it, John wonders, that Grandpa can "see" so many things?

Of all the houses that I know, I like my grandpa's best. My friend Peter has a new glass house with garden paths that go nowhere. And Maggie lives next door in an old wooden house with rooms behind rooms, all with carved doors. They are fine houses. But Grandpa's house is my favorite, because I see it through Grandpa's eyes.

Grandpa is blind. He doesn't see the house the way I do. He has his own way of seeing.

In the morning, the sun pushes through the curtains into my eyes. I burrow down into the covers to get away, but the light follows me. I give up, throw back the covers, and run to Grandpa's room.

The sun wakes Grandpa differently from the way it wakes me. He says it touches him, *warming* him awake. When I look in the room, Grandpa is already up and doing his morning exercises, bending and stretching by the bed. He stops and smiles because he hears me.

"Good morning, John."

"Where's Nana?" I ask him.

"Don't you know?" he says, bending and stretching. "Close your eyes, John, and look through my eyes."

I close my eyes. Down below, I hear the banging of pots and the sound of water running that I didn't hear before.

"Nana is in the kitchen, making breakfast," I say.

When I open my eyes again, I can see Grandpa nodding at me. He is tall with dark gray hair. And his eyes are sharp blue even though they are not sharp seeing.

I exercise with Grandpa. Up and down. Then I try to exercise with my eyes closed.

"One, two," says Grandpa, "three, four."

"Wait!" I cry. I am still on one, two when Grandpa is on three, four.

I fall sideways. Three times. Grandpa laughs as he hears me falling on the floor.

"Breakfast!" calls Nana from downstairs.

"I smell eggs frying," says Grandpa. He bends his head close to mine. "And buttered toast."

The wooden banister on the stairway has worn smooth from Grandpa running his fingers up and down. I walk behind him, my fingers following Grandpa's smooth path.

We go into the kitchen.

"I smell flowers," says Grandpa.

"What flowers?" I ask.

He smiles. He loves guessing games.

"Not violets, John, not peonies. . . ."

"Carnations!" I cry. *I* love guessing games.

"Silly." Grandpa laughs. "Marigolds. Right, Nana?"

Nana laughs, too.

"That's too easy," she says, putting two plates of food in front of us.

"It's not too easy," I say. "How can Grandpa tell? All the smells mix together in the air."

"Close your eyes, John," says Nana. "Tell me what breakfast is."

"I smell the eggs. I smell the toast," I say, my eyes closed, "and something else. The something else doesn't smell good."

"*That* something else," says Nana, smiling, "is the marigolds."

When he eats, Grandpa's plate of food is a clock.

"Two eggs at nine o'clock and toast at two o'clock," says Nana to Grandpa. "And a dollop of jam."

"A dollop of jam," I tell Grandpa, "at six o'clock."

I make my plate of food a clock, too, and eat through Grandpa's eyes.

After breakfast, I follow Grandpa's path through the dining room to the living room, to the window that he opens to feel the weather outside, and to the corner where he finds his cello.

"Will you play with me, John?" he asks.

He tunes our cellos without looking. I play with music before me, but Grandpa plays by ear.

"Listen," says Grandpa. "I'll play a piece I learned when I was young. It was my favorite."

He plays the tune while I listen. That is the way Grandpa learns new pieces — by listening.

"Now," says Grandpa. "Let's do it together."

"That's fine," says Grandpa as we play.

Later, Nana brings out her clay to sculpt my grandpa's head.

"Sit still," she says sternly.

"I won't," he says, imitating her stern voice, making us laugh.

While she works, Grandpa takes out his piece of wood. He holds it when he's thinking. His fingers move across the wood, making smooth paths like the ones on the stair banister.

"May I have a piece of thinking wood, too?" I ask.

Grandpa reaches in his shirt pocket and tosses a small bit of wood in my direction. I catch it. It is smooth with no splinters.

"The river is up," says Nana.

Grandpa nods. "It rained again last night. Did you hear the gurgling in the rain gutter?"

As they talk, my fingers begin a river on my thinking wood. The wood will winter in my pocket so when I am not at Grandpa's house I can still think about Nana, Grandpa, and the river.

When Nana is finished working, Grandpa runs his hand over the sculpture, his fingers soft and quick like butterflies.

"It looks like me," he says, surprised.

My eyes have already told me that the sculpture looks like Grandpa. But he shows me how to feel his face with my three middle fingers and then feel the clay face.

"Pretend your fingers are water," he tells me.

My waterfall fingers flow down his clay head, filling in the spaces under the eyes like little pools before they flow over the cheeks. It does feel like Grandpa. This time my fingers tell me.

Grandpa and I walk outside, through the front yard and across the field to the river. Grandpa has not always been blind. He remembers in his mind the shining of the sun on the river, the violets in the meadow, and every marigold in his garden. But he gently takes my arm as we walk so that I can help show him the path.

"I feel a south wind," says Grandpa.

I can tell which way the wind is blowing because
I see the way the tops of the trees are bending.

Grandpa tells by the feel of the meadow grasses and by the way his hair blows against his face.

When we come to the riverbank, I see that Nana was right. The water is high. I see a blackbird with a red patch on its wing sitting on a cattail. Without thinking, I point my finger.

"What is that bird, Grandpa?" I ask excitedly.

"Conk-a-ree," the bird calls to us.

"A red-winged blackbird," says Grandpa quickly.

He can't see my finger pointing, but he hears the song of the bird.

"And somewhere behind the blackbird," he says, listening, "there's a robin."

I hear another song and I look and look until I see the robin that Grandpa knows is here.

Nana calls from the front porch of the house.

"Nana's made hot bread for lunch," he tells me happily, "and spice tea." Spice tea is his favorite.

I close my eyes, but all I can smell is the wet earth by the river.

As we walk back to the house, Grandpa stops suddenly. He bends his head to one side, listening. He points his finger toward the sky.

"Honkers," he whispers.

I look up and see a flock of geese, high in the clouds, flying in a V.

"Canada geese," I tell him.

"Honkers," he says again, and we both laugh.

We walk up the path again and to the yard where Nana is painting the porch chairs. Grandpa smells the paint.

"What color, Nana?" he asks. "I cannot smell the color."

"Blue," I say, smiling. "Blue like the sky."

"Blue like the color of Grandpa's eyes," Nana says.

When he was younger, before I can remember, before he was blind, Grandpa did things the way I do. Now, when we drink tea and eat lunch on the porch, Grandpa pours his own cup of tea by putting his finger just inside the top of the cup to tell him when it is full. He never burns his finger.

Later, when I wash the dishes, he feels them as he dries them. He even sends some back for me to wash again.

"Next time," says Grandpa, pretending to be cross, "I wash, you dry."

In the afternoon, Grandpa, Nana, and I take our books outside to read under the apple tree. Grandpa reads his book with his fingers, feeling the raised Braille dots that tell him the words.

As he reads, Grandpa laughs out loud.

"Tell us what's funny," says Nana. "Read to us."

And he does.

Nana and I put down our books to listen. A squirrel comes down the trunk of the apple tree and seems to listen, too. But Grandpa doesn't see him.

After supper, Grandpa turns on the television. I watch, but Grandpa listens, and the music and the words tell him when something is dangerous or funny, happy or sad.

Somehow, Grandpa knows when it is dark, and he takes me upstairs. When I get into bed, he bends down to kiss me, his hands feeling my head.

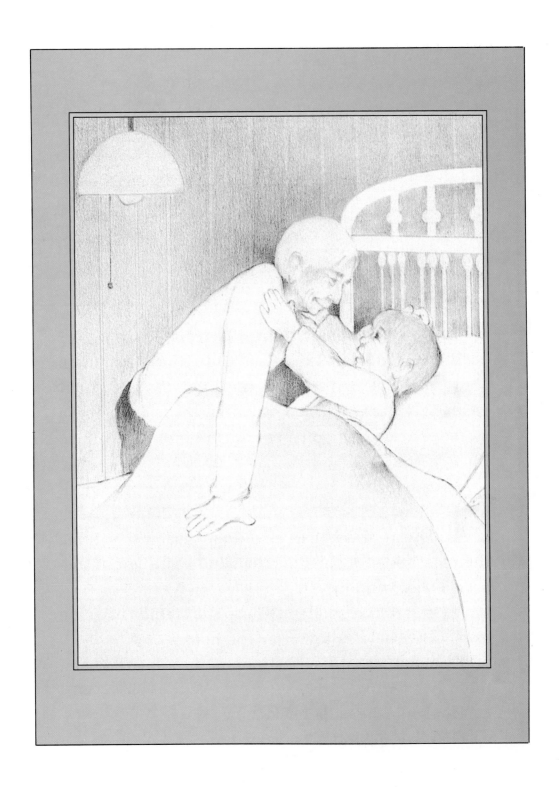

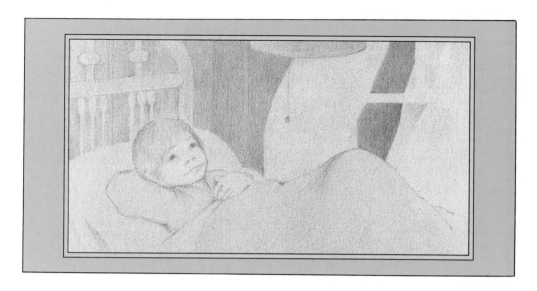

"You need a haircut, John," he says.

Before Grandpa leaves, he pulls the light chain above my bed to turn out the light. But, without meaning to, he's turned it on instead. I lie for a moment after he's gone, smiling, before I get up to turn off the light.

Then, when it is dark for me the way it is dark for Grandpa, I hear the night noises that Grandpa hears. I hear the house creaking, the birds singing their last songs of the day, the wind rustling the tree outside my window.

Then, all of a sudden, I hear the sounds of geese overhead. They fly low over the house.

"Grandpa," I call softly, hoping he's heard them, too.

"Honkers," he calls back.

"Go to sleep, John," says Nana.

Grandpa says her voice smiles to him. I test it.
"What?" I call to her.
"I said go to sleep," she answers.

She says it sternly, but Grandpa is right. Her voice smiles to me. I know, because I'm looking through Grandpa's eyes.

Author

Through Grandpa's Eyes is the second book written by Patricia MacLachlan. She used her experiences as a member of a local family service agency in writing it. She wanted to show the special relationship between young people and older people. Ms. MacLachlan has also been an English teacher.

Summary Questions

John learned to see things "through Grandpa's eyes." Use these questions to tell how this happened.

1. How and what did Grandpa "see"?
2. What did John learn from Grandpa about seeing?
3. Tell what John "saw" with his ears, his hands, his nose, and his mouth during his day with Grandpa.

The Reading and Writing Connection

Grandpa and John did the things named below together.

read books   took a walk
did exercises   played the cello

Which of these things do you think was the most fun for John? Write a paragraph that tells why you think John had fun doing it. Try to use some words from the box.

exercises	**cello**	**tunes**
imitating	**rustling**	**creaking**
flock	**smooth**	

Night
by Sara Teasdale

Stars over snow
        And in the west a planet
Swinging below a star —
        Look for a lovely thing and you will
                find it,
It is not far —
        It never will be far.

Sensory Images

You can paint a word picture to help others "see" what it is you are telling about. To do this use picture words.

Picture words help you to see and feel more clearly what is happening in a story.

The word *burrow* is a good example of a picture word.

Read the following sentence:

I *burrow* down into the covers to get warm.

The word *burrow* helps you to "see" someone digging deeper and deeper under the covers.

Now read the following story. As you read, look for the picture words.

I love Grandmother's kitchen when the morning sun pushes through the curtains and spreads like warm butter on the floor. While I eat my breakfast, I name the flowers in the painting hanging over the table. On top of a table near the window are tall glass jars with yellow caps. Inside the jars, Grandmother keeps dry foods like rice and nuts. One jar is filled with dried fruits. I like to spend the morning at Grandmother's because it's such a pleasant place.

Now draw a picture for the story about Grandmother's kitchen. Share your picture with others. Tell which words, or groups of words, in the story helped you to "see" the picture.

Something Extra

Pretend that you have seen one of the following things shown in the photographs on this page. Write a paragraph to describe what you have seen.

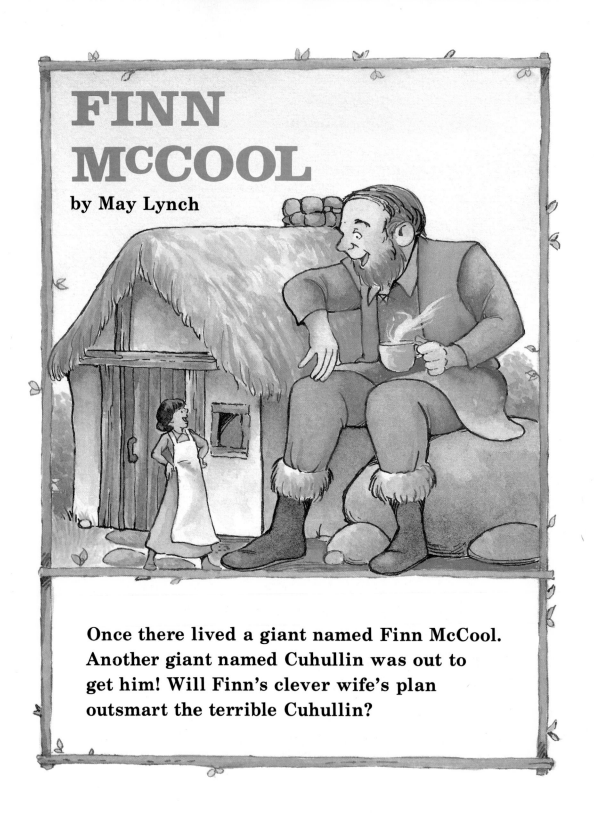

FINN McCOOL

by May Lynch

Once there lived a giant named Finn McCool. Another giant named Cuhullin was out to get him! Will Finn's clever wife's plan outsmart the terrible Cuhullin?

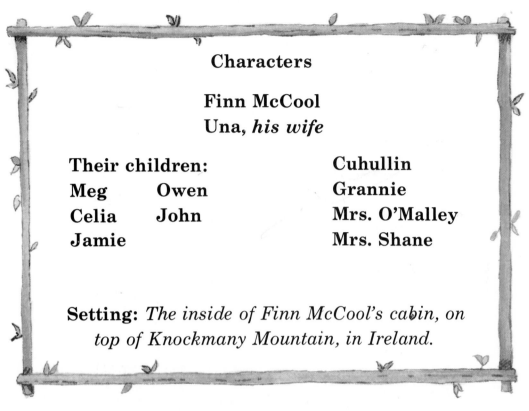

Characters

Finn McCool
Una, *his wife*

Their children:
Meg   Owen
Celia   John
Jamie

Cuhullin
Grannie
Mrs. O'Malley
Mrs. Shane

Setting: *The inside of Finn McCool's cabin, on top of Knockmany Mountain, in Ireland.*

As the play begins, **Una** *is standing at a wash tub washing out a piece of clothing. She places it on top of a basket of clothes at her feet.* **Owen,** **Jamie,** *and* **John** *are sitting nearby.*

Una: There! That's the last of my washing, and I must say it was a big one.

Owen: I'll say it was. I carried six pails of water up Knockmany Mountain this morning.

John: And so did Jamie and I. We do it all the time.

Una: My, I'll be glad when your father, Finn McCool, finds us a spring up here near the house.

John: He says there's water right out there under those two rocks.

Jamie: Yes, and he says he's going to move the rocks someday.

Owen: Someday! He keeps saying *someday*, but *someday* never comes.

Una: Owen McCool, don't speak that way. After all, the dear man is very busy and tired — and — and busy. *(Meg and Celia enter.)*

Celia: Mother! Mother! Guess what!

Meg: Grannie Owen and Mrs. O'Malley and Mrs. Shane are coming up Knockmany Mountain right now.

Una: Your grannie hasn't been here in a long time. Put on the teakettle, Meg. Celia, dear, lay the cloth. And Owen and Jamie, hang these things out on the line like good boys. *(Jamie and Owen take the basket of clothes and exit.)*

John: I'll fix the fire. *(Una and the girls clean up the room as John takes care of the fireplace.)*

Celia *(At the window):* Here they are. I see them coming up the path.

John *(Opening the door):* Welcome, Grannie. Good day, Mrs. Shane. Good day to you, too, Mrs. O'Malley. *(Grannie, Mrs. O'Malley, and Mrs. Shane enter and all say hello to each other. The girls hug Grannie.)*

Grannie: Well, I must say, Knockmany Mountain gets steeper every year. I'm out of breath from that long walk.

Mrs. O'Malley: I am, too, and that wind gets stronger and stronger.

Mrs. Shane: Una, however do you manage in winter when that cold wind howls and blows and screams? Aren't you afraid to be up here?

Una *(Laughing):* No, I'm not. Finn McCool wouldn't live anywhere else in the world.

Grannie: Where is Finn today?

John: He's somewhere about. He's busy, I guess.

Mrs. Shane: It's too bad he's too busy to find a spring up here. Those poor children of yours shouldn't have to carry water all the way up the mountain.

John: We really like to do that, Mrs. Shane. Besides, our father says that someday he is going to let us help him split open those rocks out there. There's water under them. *(The women shake their heads.)*

Meg: Grannie, Mother, Mrs. O'Malley, Mrs. Shane, do sit down and have a cup of tea. *(The women sit down as the girls serve them tea.)*

Grannie: It's so good to see you, Una. Since Finn built this house up on top of the world, we hardly ever get together.

Mrs. Shane: Is it true, Una, that Finn came up here to get away from Cuhullin?

Una: Oh my, no.

John: Who is Cuhullin?

Mrs. O'Malley *(Quickly):* Nobody important, John.

Mrs. Shane: *Nobody important?* He's a giant. That's who he is.

John: Finn McCool, our father, is a giant too.

Mrs. Shane: Oh, but Cuhullin is very strong. There's no one as strong within a hundred miles of our town of Dungannon.

Grannie: Except maybe my son-in-law, Finn McCool.

Mrs. Shane: The talk around Dungannon right now is that Cuhullin once stamped his foot and all of Ireland shook and trembled.

John: Why would he do that?

Mrs. Shane: To show that he had beaten every single giant in Ireland except Finn McCool. He can't ever seem to find Finn.

Mrs. O'Malley *(Upset):* I don't like to frighten you, Una, but there is talk in town that Cuhullin is on his way here to find Finn.

Mrs. Shane: They say he'll stamp Finn into pancakes when he finds him.

John: But why?

Grannie: It's an old story, John. Finn used to brag about how much stronger he was than Cuhullin. Of course, Cuhullin heard about it, and he began to look for Finn McCool.

Mrs. O'Malley: And he's never found him.

Una: Why, we have nothing to be afraid of. Finn will take care of us. But I just remembered I must do some baking.

John: You just did your week's baking, Mother. (**Una** *starts to mix flour and salt in a bowl, as* **Grannie** *and other women rise.*)

Una: Did I indeed, John? *(To the women)* Must you go so soon? *(They nod and start toward door.)* Finn will be sorry he wasn't here to see you. Come again soon.

Grannie: We will, Una. *(They exit.)*

Una *(To herself)*: I need some iron skillets. *(She picks up two skillets)* Here they are.

Meg: I'm scared, Mother.

Una *(To herself)*: One bite of bread with a skillet in it will take care of Cuhullin. *(She starts to cover the skillets with dough.* **Finn** *enters.)*

Finn: I'm frightened! I've been to Dungannon and the giant Cuhullin is on his way to town looking for me. He told somebody he'd turn me into pancakes. What ever will I do if he finds me?

Una: You leave everything to me, Finn. I'll handle Cuhullin. Meg, give your father that old long nightgown of mine and find that baby's bonnet in the drawer. *(To* **Finn***)* And *you* put on the nightgown and the bonnet and hide in that bed over there. *(She puts the bread into the oven.* **Meg** *exits.)*

Finn: Right here? Hide here in the open? *(Una nods her head.* **Finn** *exits and returns dressed in a long white nightgown and a bonnet. He climbs into bed, as* **Meg** *re-enters.)*

Una: Girls, get Jamie and Owen and gather lots of wood. Then build up a big fire right on the very tip of Knockmany Mountain.

Celia: But a fire on the mountain means that we are welcoming a stranger. The only stranger is — is Cuhullin.

Meg: I'm too scared to move.

Una: Go! Get your brothers to help you. John, as soon as you see Cuhullin coming up the mountain, you must let out a long, loud whistle.

Finn: *Ooooh! Ooooh!* I'm scared out of my mind. He'll be here any minute!

Una: Nonsense! You just listen to my plan. I've already made bread that Cuhullin will never forget, and now if I take some cheese and make it look like a stone — *(She sits on the edge of the bed and whispers in* **Finn**'s *ear. Then both of them laugh out loud. She whispers again, pointing to the oven. A loud whistle is heard.)* Cuhullin is coming! Now keep your hat on and remember *who* you are! *(She hands him a stone and a round cheese from the table.)* Now, don't roll on this cheese. *(A great banging at the door can be heard.)*

Cuhullin *(Shouting from offstage):* Is this where you live, Finn McCool? Open up! *(Una opens the door and looks surprised.)*

Una: Well, I wondered if I heard someone at the door. Come in stranger. It's so windy I don't always hear people knocking. Welcome.

Cuhullin *(Entering):* Does Finn McCool live here?

Una *(Sweetly):* He does, indeed.

Cuhullin: Is he home?

Una: Dear me, no! He left here a while ago. Somebody said a giant named Cuhullin was down in Dungannon looking for him. Finn went right down to make pudding out of him.

Cuhullin: *Hm-m-m.*

Una: Did you ever hear of Cuhullin, poor thing?

Cuhullin: That's me.

Una: Oh, you poor man. Finn is in a terrible temper. Don't let him find you.

Cuhullin: I've been wanting to meet him for years, but I notice he doesn't let me find him.

Una: Well, wait for him then, but don't say I didn't warn you.

Cuhullin: I'll wait.

Una: While you're waiting, to keep yourself from being scared, would you mind turning the house around? Finn always turns it around in the fall when the wind blows at the door. It makes it warmer in winter.

Cuhullin: Turn the house? Nothing easier. *(He exits. A loud noise is heard from offstage. Una goes to the door.* **Finn** *groans.)*

Una *(Calling):* That's better. Thank you very much. Now, would you do something else? Finn has been meaning to pull those rocks apart and find us a spring, but he hurried off, and I do need water. *(She steps back toward* **Finn** *as a loud crash is heard.)* Oh, my! He pulled apart those rocks with his bare hands and made a spring! *(***Finn*** groans.* **Cuhullin** *enters.)*

Cuhullin: What now?

Una: That's a good little job finished. Now you come and have a bite to eat. Even though you think Finn is your enemy, he would want me to be kind to anyone in our home. Here's a cup of tea, and I have some hot bread in the oven. *(She takes out loaves of bread.* **Cuhullin** *bites into the bread.)*

Cuhullin *(Groaning):* I just broke my two front teeth! What did you give me to eat?

Una: Only what Finn always eats. He and our little child in the bed have this bread all the time. *(She points to the bed.)* Here, why don't you try another one?

Cuhullin: Jumping shamrocks! My teeth are ruined! Take this stuff away. What a toothache! *(He holds his jaw.)*

Finn: *(In a deep voice):* Give me something to eat. I'm hungry. (**Una** *takes a loaf of bread to* **Finn**, *and he pretends to eat it.)* Mm-m-m-m!

Cuhullin *(Surprised):* I'd like to see that child. He must be some boy!

Una: Get up, dearie, and show the man that you're Finn's little boy.

Cuhullin: Toads and snakes! What a huge child!

Finn: Are you strong? Can you squeeze water from a stone? My father can, and so can I. *(He hands a stone to* **Cuhullin**, *who squeezes it.)* Ah, you *can't* do it. (**Finn** *takes the stone, throws it on the bed, then picks up the cheese, unseen by* **Cu-hullin**, *and squeezes it until water comes out of it.)* My father, Finn McCool, taught me to do that. He can stamp a giant to pancakes.

Una: Into bed, son, so you'll be big and strong.

Cuhullin *(upset):* I think I'd better go. I never saw the likes of that child. If he can squeeze water from a stone, what must his father be like!

Finn: Will Father hurt that little man, Mother?

Una: No, dearie. *(To **Cuhullin**)* You are lucky that Finn isn't home. That temper of his! *(**Cuhullin** exits, running. **Finn** and **Una** laugh. The children enter.)*

Meg: Mother, what did you do to Cuhullin?

John: He was holding his jaw and crying about a toothache.

Jamie: I watched from the bushes. He pulled those rocks apart one — two — three. And now we have a spring.

Una: And he turned the house around. It's warmer already.

Meg: How did you do it, Mother?

Finn: Ah, your mother is a clever woman. She makes rocks out of cheese.

Una: Your father fooled him. Cuhullin tried to squeeze water from a rock, but Finn squeezed water from *cheese.* Cuhullin never knew the difference.

Finn: And she put iron skillets into her bread and served it to Cuhullin.

Una: But your father fooled him. He just nibbled around the edge and pretended to eat it.

Owen: Why are you wearing that silly outfit, Father?

Una: You should have seen how your father fooled Cuhullin, pretending he was a baby giant. *(They all laugh.)*

Finn: Now if somebody will help me out of this nightgown, I'll lie down and have a rest. A man as busy as I am gets very tired.

(Curtain)

Author

May Lynch, the author of the play you have just read, has been an elementary school teacher for many years. She has written a number of short plays based on subjects popular with the children in her classroom.

Summary Questions

Finn McCool had a big problem – Cuhullin! Use the questions to tell how the problem was solved.

1. Cuhullin was looking for Finn McCool. Why was that a big problem for Finn?
2. Who solved Finn's problem by outsmarting Cuhullin? How?
3. Do you think Cuhullin will ever set out to get Finn McCool again? Why or why not?

4. Imagine that you are Cuhullin. Tell a friend what you think of Finn McCool now.

The Reading and Writing Connection

Una fooled Cuhullin with some clever ideas. She used the things pictured below in unusual ways.

Which idea do you think was the most clever? Write a paragraph that tells why you think this idea was so clever. Try to use some words from the box.

clever	**iron**	**nonsense**
ruin	**tremble**	**skillet**
spring	**brag**	

Using a Glossary

You have learned that often when you come to a new word, or a word you haven't seen before, you can use the context to help you learn something about the meaning.

For example, suppose you did not know the meaning of the word *ketch*. Would you get many clues from the other words in this sentence?

The beautiful **ketch** glided slowly across the calm sea.

The context in that sentence gives you a good idea that a *ketch* is probably a kind of boat. But suppose you wanted to know exactly what kind of boat it was. The context does not tell you that. If you need to know exactly what a word means, you can use a dictionary or a glossary.

A **dictionary** is a book that lists many, many words and their meanings. A **glossary** is also a list of words and their meanings. It can be found in the back of many books. But only those words that are likely to be new to you *in that book* will be found in a glossary. There is a glossary in the back of this book beginning on page 368.

Entry Words

The words that have meanings given in a dictionary or a glossary are called **entry words**. Each entry word is presented in boldface type. The words in a dictionary and a glossary are listed in alphabetical order.

For example, if you looked up the word *ketch* in the glossary, this is what you might see:

ketch   A sailboat that has two masts, or poles, that support the sails; the taller mast is toward the front of the boat.

Now do you know what a *ketch* is?

Locating the Entry Words

Because the entry words are listed in alphabetical order, you can save time by opening a dictionary or a glossary near the word that you want to find.

Decide whether the word you are looking for begins with a letter that comes near the beginning, middle, or end of the alphabet. Then open the dictionary or glossary near the beginning, the middle, or the end.

Guide Words

After you have opened a dictionary or glossary near the word that you want, you can then use **guide words** to find the page on which that word appears. Guide words are given at the top of each page. They are printed in boldface type and look like this:

improve / loaf

The word on the left tells you the first entry word on that page. The word on the right tells you the last entry word on that page. All entry words that come between those two in alphabetical order will be found on that page.

Look at the guide words again. Would you find the word *ketch* on that page? Would you find *marigold*?

Base Words

Most glossaries list only base words as entry words. You know that a base word may have an ending added to it. The base word for *appeared* or *appearing* is *appear*. If you need to find the meaning of a word to which an ending has been added, look for the base word in the glossary.

If you come to a new word that is not listed in the glossary, you should use a dictionary.

Using the Glossary

Read the sentences below. Use the glossary at the back of this book to find the meaning of each boldface word.

1. The box is in the **attic.**
2. The **gosling** swims here.
3. We heard the **wail** of the coyote.
4. They **gazed** at the stars.

Now can you tell in your own words what each boldface word means?

Skill Summary

- A dictionary is a book that gives the meanings of many, many words.
- A glossary at the back of a book gives the meanings of some of the words used in that book.
- Entry words are listed in alphabetical order. Usually only base words are listed as entry words.
- Guide words at the top of each page show the first and last entry words on that page. The word you are looking for will be on the page where it would come, in alphabetical order, between the guide words.
- Knowing whether a word begins with a letter near the beginning, middle, or end of the alphabet helps you decide whether to open the dictionary or glossary near the beginning, the middle, or the end.

Digging Up Dinosaurs

by Aliki

Many people enjoy looking at dinosaur skeletons in museums. Where do scientists find the bones of these huge animals that lived long ago? How do the scientists put them together?

Dinosaurs lived long, long ago. A few of them were as small as birds, but most were enormous. Some dinosaurs ate plants, while others were meat-eaters.

Dinosaurs lived on every continent in the world. Then they died out. No one knows for sure why they became extinct, but they did.

Until about 200 years ago, no one knew anything about dinosaurs. Then people began finding things in rock. They found large footprints, huge mysterious bones, and strange teeth. People were finding fossils. Fossils are a kind of diary of the past. They are the remains of plants and animals that lived long ago. Instead of rotting or crumbling away, the remains were preserved and slowly turned to stone.

What a discovery these fossils were! But digging up dinosaur bones was not an easy job. The bones had to be dug out of the ground, slowly and carefully.

Even today, digging up dinosaurs is not an easy job. A team of experts must work together.

First, they have to find a spot where a dinosaur once lived. The spot may be in a deep quarry, on a high cliff, or in a steep canyon.

Scientist in Montana working with dinosaur fossils

Scientist exploring site where there might be fossils

With luck, someone will spot a fossil bone poking through the rock. The place where the team will be working is covered with a tent, and the work begins.

Sometimes the fossil is buried so deeply that the rock around it has to be drilled or blasted. Then thousands of pounds of broken rocks are taken away. Scientists chip at the rock close to the fossil; then very carefully they brush away the sand and bits of stone.

As soon as a bone is uncovered, it is brushed with hobby glue. The glue helps hold the bone together so that it won't crumble. Then the bone is numbered, to help scientists remember where each bone belongs.

Site in Arizona where scientists are working with fossils

Brushing sand from fossils

Painting fossil with hobby glue

Putting plaster cast on fossil

Fossil being removed

Sometimes a skeleton has to be cut apart so that it can be moved. The draftsperson draws each bone in its exact position, and the photographer takes pictures. That way, there can be no mix-up later when someone tries to put the skeleton together.

When the bones are ready to be moved, they are carefully wrapped. Small bones are wrapped in tissue paper and put into boxes or sacks.

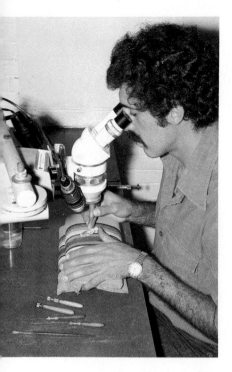

Scientist using a microscope to examine bone fragments

Large bones are left half-buried in rock. They will be dug out later, in the museum. Each fossil is covered with a plaster cast.

The bones are then packed in straw, placed in crates, and taken to the museum.

At the museum, scientists finish digging the bones out of the rock. Then they study the bones.

Scientists compare the bones with the bones of other dinosaurs. They compare them with the bones of other animals. Scientists try to discover what size and shape the dinosaur was. They are also interested in finding out how the dinosaur stood and walked and what it ate.

Scientist classifying dinosaur bones

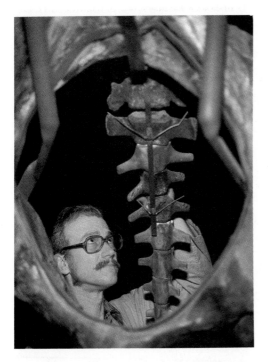 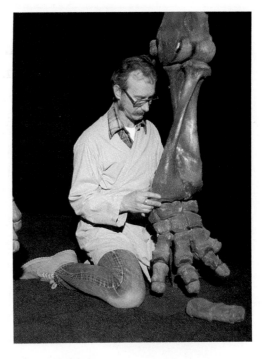

Scientist assembling skeleton of a dinosaur

Scientist positioning foot of a dinosaur

If there are enough bones, scientists are able to build a complete skeleton. A frame is made in the shape of the dinosaur to help hold up the bones. Then the bones are wired together, one by one. They are held in place with pieces of metal. If any bones are missing, plastic or fiber glass ones are made to replace them. You can hardly tell the new bones from the old ones.

After many months, the work is complete. The dinosaur skeleton looks just as it once did long, long ago.

At one time, only a few museums had dinosaur skeletons. Then scientists learned to make copies of the skeletons. A copy is difficult to make, and it takes a long time. The original skeleton has to be taken apart, bone by bone. Copies of the bones are made out of fiber glass.

The new fiber glass bones are put together to make a copy of the original skeleton. A fiber glass dinosaur skeleton is much like the original, but it is much stronger and lighter.

Completed dinosaur skeleton at a museum in Chicago, Illinois

Brontosaurus skeleton and Stegosaurus skeleton at a museum in New York City

Now museums all over the world have dinosaur skeletons. Many people spend hours looking at and studying these skeletons.

Author

Aliki, Mrs. Franz Brandenburg, is the author of over twenty children's books, some of them award winners. She has been an art teacher and a book illustrator. Her two young children introduced her to dinosaurs. Much later, when they were grown up, she wrote the book she wished she had had then to answer some of their questions.

Selection Wrap-up

Summary Questions

Some scientists dig up dinosaur bones, or fossils. Use these questions to tell how and why.

1. Where do scientists find fossils? How do they dig them up?
2. What do scientists do with the dinosaur bones?
3. Why do you think scientists dig up the bones?
4. Imagine that you are a guide in a science museum. Explain how scientists get dinosaur bones safely to the museum, and what happens to the bones there.

The Reading and Writing Connection

Look at the pictures of the dinosaurs on page 93. Choose one and write about it. Tell about its size, its color, when it lived, and what you think it ate. Try to use some words from the box.

skeletons	extinct	remains
enormous	fossils	preserved
discovery	continent	scientists

Dinosaurs

Cimolopteryx

Ammosaurus

Thescelosaurus

Tyrannosaurus rex

Triceratops

Gorgosaurus

Trachodon

Trionyx

Anatosaurus

Leidyosuchus

Coniophis

93

My Dinosaur's Day at the Park

by Elizabeth Winthrop

My pet dinosaur got in trouble
When we went for a walk in the park.
I took off his leash and let him run free.
He didn't come back until dark.

He ate up the new row of oak trees
(The gardener was fit to be tied).
Then he stopped in the playground and bent down his head
And the kids used his neck for a slide.

He knocked down the fence by the boat pond
With a swing of his twenty-foot tail;
When he stopped to explain he was sorry,
His legs blocked the bicycle trail.

When the sun set, my dino got worried;
He's always been scared of the dark.
He sat down on the ground and started to cry.
His tears flooded out the whole park.

A friend of mine rowed his boat over
When he heard my pet dino's sad roar.
He showed him the way home to my house
And helped him unlock the front door.

He's a loveable, lumbering fellow
But after my pet had his spree,
They put up a sign in the park and it reads,
NO DINOS ALLOWED TO RUN FREE.

My Mother Sends Her Wisdom

**written by
Louise McClenathan**

**illustrated by
Rosekrans Hoffman**

In this Russian tale, a clever peasant woman and her daughter try to outsmart a greedy moneylender named Boris.

Old Boris is much hated in the countryside, for his loans at high interest rates often caused the small farmers to lose their land. When Katya and her mother are faced with losing their land, they plan a way to outsmart Old Boris.

How Katya's mother uses her wisdom to outsmart Old Boris makes this a very lively and interesting tale.

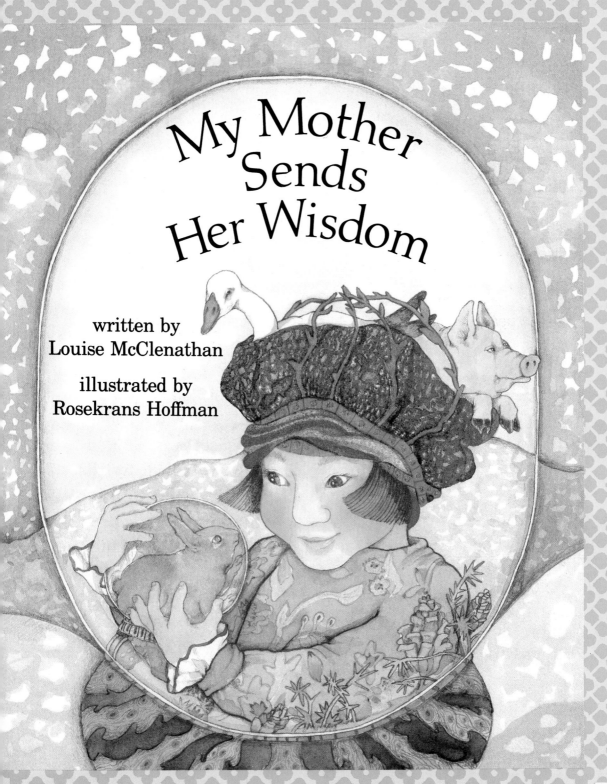

My Mother
Sends
Her Wisdom

written by
Louise McClenathan

illustrated by
Rosekrans Hoffman

"Mama," cried Katya, as she peered through the cottage window, "Old Boris, the moneylender, is coming down the road in his horse cart."

"Let him come, little one," answered Katya's mother, as she worked warm dough for bread. The dough made a soft slapping sound against the wooden table.

Boris and Alexei, the small boy who kept his accounts, drew up before the cottage, and the gentle sounds of the house were broken by the old man's loud pounding on the door. "Widow Petrovna," he shouted, "I have come to collect the monthly rubles you owe me from the loan of silver to your late husband." His eyes were yellow, like a cat's eyes, and his voice was filled with the sound of greed. Alexei stood with his account book and pen, waiting for the rubles to be dropped into his master's soft leather purse.

Mama stood behind Katya, slowly wiping her floury hands on her apron. "Tomorrow, Old Boris," she said, "I shall send you a fine plump goose and gander. My daughter will bring them to your house in the city, for the ride in your cart would upset the goose's laying. They will be my payment to you this month."

"Very well then, but no later than sundown tomorrow," Boris said.

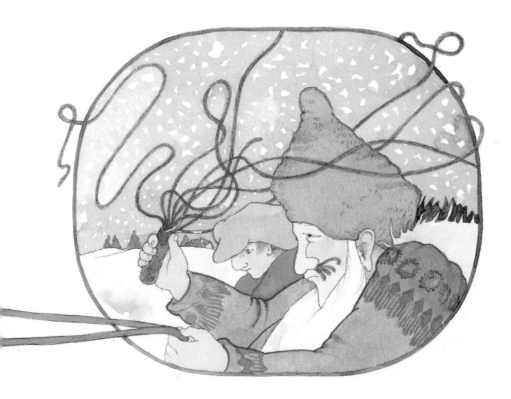

After his horse and cart disappeared down the road, Mama and Katya sat down for the evening meal. "We shall have one more egg from the good goose, Katya," Mama said cheerfully.

The child ate her soup slowly, thinking about Old Boris. He was hated in the countryside, for he would lend money to the peasant farmers at a very high interest rate and insist on collecting it even if the crops were poor. When they could not pay, he took over their farms, which he sold to the large landowners.

"Do not worry, Katya," said Mama, as she looked across the table. "I have a plan for Old Boris. If it works, we shall keep our land." While the clock ticked softly and the firelight cast shadows on the walls, Mama told Katya what to do.

They went to sleep bundled in woolens beside the great stove. The heat from the stove warmed the little girl, and she slept easily, knowing that her mother was a wise woman.

The next morning Katya ate her bowl of baked cereal and put on a warm cloak. Mama tucked a small meat-filled pie into her pocket and said, "Remember to repeat to Old Boris everything I told you. Especially to say, 'My mother sends her wisdom.' Do not forget his answer."

With a plump white goose under each arm, Katya set off through the forest. The trees were thick and the woods were still. She walked quickly, talking to the goose and gander for company, for it was lonely. There was a smell of snow in the air, and the wind moaned like a wolf crying at the moon.

Soon the forest path grew wider, and she could see the roofs of the city houses through the trees. The streets were narrow and crowded. Men pushed carts along, and women cried their wares in the marketplace. "Come buy from me, come buy from me," they chanted. "Good bread, good fowl, good brooms today." Katya wished she were back in the forest again. The city seemed so noisy and crowded.

An old woman showed her the way to the moneylender's house, which stood on a corner surrounded by a fence. Katya managed to unhook the gate and lifted the great brass doorknocker. Alexei peered out and went to get his master. Soon Boris came to the door and opened it wide. Alexei stood behind him. "So you have brought my birds, and high time," snapped the old man.

"Yes, here are the geese for payment, and my mother sends her wisdom," said Katya in a trembling voice.

"Wisdom, is it?" said Old Boris with a laugh.

103

Katya's eyes were bright as she recited what her mother had taught her:

"Two well-kept geese, so I've been told,
May truly lay fine eggs of gold."

Boris shook his head and sneered. "What do I need with the wisdom of a peasant woman? Alexei, mark these geese in the book as payment, then take them to the market to sell."

Katya started for home at once. Without the geese to care for, the journey went quickly.

"And did Old Boris accept my wisdom?" asked Mama, as Katya took off her cloak.

"He laughed, Mama, and said he did not need the wisdom of a peasant woman. Then he ordered the goose and gander sold at the market."

"We shall see, we shall see," Mama said softly, as she warmed the child's feet before the stove.

The next month, on the day payment was due, Katya took two plump pigs through the forest to the moneylender. She kept them moving with her hooked stick, poking them when they stopped to root in the rich, dark earth.

"Come pig, pig, pig. Come pig, pig, pig," she chanted, and soon they arrived in the city. The sun was high overhead when she reached the moneylender's house. This time Alexei opened the door, and his master wandered out. "Here are two pigs for payment, and my mother sends her wisdom," said Katya, as the pigs rooted in the garden.

"What, your mother's wisdom again?" Boris asked scornfully.

Katya drew a deep breath and spoke quickly:

"Five pink piglets, born anew,
Will squeal much more than old ones do."

The old man threw back his head and laughed. "If your mother were wise, she would not owe me money. It is the peasant who squeals, not the pig."

Katya did not answer, but turned and quickly went on her way. Soon she was back in the quiet forest, which seemed safer than the noisy, crowded city. When she returned home, she told her mother what Old Boris had answered.

"Good," said Mama, "all is going well, little one."

In spring, on the day the next payment was due, Katya woke up early. As rays of sunlight splintered the early morning sky, Mama stood by the stove making breakfast.

"Today, Katya, you will take a good sack of wheat to Old Boris," Mama said. "It is heavy, so you must pull it in the little cart and take the dog with you for company."

They loaded the small cart with the wheat, and again Katya set off. She entered the forest with the cart behind her and the dog running ahead.

It was cool and the birds sang; bright patches of sunlight filtered through the leaves. The dog chased a rabbit, then returned and tugged at Katya's skirts to hurry her along. "I'm coming, I'm coming," she said with a laugh.

At high noon, she knocked on the money-lender's door and presented the grain. "Here is a sack of wheat for payment, and my mother sends her wisdom."

"What nonsense this time?" asked Old Boris, and Katya recited her mother's riddle:

"How is it that ten grains of wheat
  Could give us all enough to eat?"

"I laugh at your mother's wisdom," snapped Old Boris. "She may keep it for herself. Alexei, mark the book for Widow Petrovna and take the wheat to market for sale."

Once more Katya went home and told her mother what the old man had said.

"Now we shall see who is the wiser, daughter," said her mother with a smile, and the two set to work in the garden.

The next month Katya did not visit the moneylender, and one day Old Boris and Alexei came to the cottage and knocked on the door. "You are late with your payment, Widow Petrovna," said the old man. "Do you have nothing to pay this month?"

Mama looked at him sternly and spoke in a clear voice. "You are wrong, Old Boris, for my debt is paid off."

"Paid off, indeed! You still owe twenty rubles, either in money or in goods. Check the book, Alexei."

The boy turned the pages of the heavy book and read the figures. "Twenty rubles still owed, master."

The widow shook her head. "My debt is paid. The sack of wheat was the last payment, and you shall get nothing more. You must go to Judge Petruschka to ask for a hearing against me if you do not believe it, Boris."

"I shall, I shall," said the old man, nodding. "He will find that you are still owing, and I shall insist upon taking your land in payment," and he drove off down the road in a cloud of dust.

Soon the day came when Judge Petruschka held court. Old Boris and Alexei sat on one side of the room, while Katya and her mother sat on the other.

111

"What is the charge?" the judge asked quietly.

"This woman says she has paid her debt, but she still owes me twenty rubles," said Boris.

"What has she paid you?" the judge asked.

"Two geese, which sold for six rubles. Two pigs, which brought ten rubles at market. A sack of wheat, which sold for four rubles."

"Is this true, Widow Petrovna?" the judge asked.

"No, your honor, it is only half true. My daughter will tell you what she offered Old Boris each time she took payment to him."

Katya stood before the judge and spoke out bravely. "When I took two geese, I offered him my mother's wisdom in this riddle:

'Two well-kept geese, so I've been told,
May truly lay fine eggs of gold.'

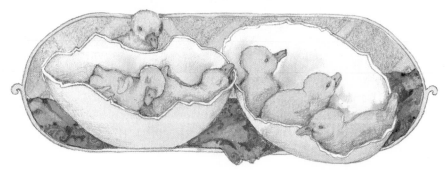

"He did not accept my mother's wisdom. If he had, he would have kept the goose and gander, collected many eggs, raised a flock of goslings, and sold them at market for three times what he received.

"When I took the pigs to him, I offered him more of my mother's wisdom in this riddle:

'Five pink piglets, born anew,
    Will squeal much more than old ones do.'

"If he had kept the pigs and raised a litter of five piglets, he could have sold them for twice as much as the two pigs brought.

113

"The third time I offered my mother's wisdom in this riddle:

'How is it that ten grains of wheat
Could give us all enough to eat?'

"He could have sold half the wheat for payment, planted the rest, and had a field of wheat next year, two fields after that, and four the following year."

The judge looked thoughtful. "Is it true, Old Boris, this story the child tells?"

Boris stared at him angrily. "Wisdom is not the same as money," he said.

The judge sat for a moment, scratching some figures in his book with a long pen. "Such wisdom," he said slowly, "is what feeds us all. I find, Old Boris, that Widow Petrovna has overpaid you some thirty rubles in her wisdom, so it is you who owes her money. I order you to pay her."

The judge would not be moved, though the old man flew into a rage. Finally he drew the money from his purse and threw it on the table.

Katya was trembling, but as she looked at the judge's face she thought she saw a tiny smile hiding around the corners of his mouth.

Soon all the countryside knew that Old Boris had been outdone by the wit of a peasant woman. Friends and relatives came to celebrate, bringing cream from their cows, flowers from their fields, and good tea to drink. "We share your joy, Widow Petrovna," they said. "May your land blossom with good fortune always."

Author

Louise McClenathan, who has been called a master storyteller, wrote *My Mother Sends Her Wisdom* in 1979. The idea for the story came from something that happened to a friend's mother. Family traditions or customs interest Ms. McClenathan very much. She has been a reading specialist in Virginia as well as a college planning officer in Pennsylvania. She has written a great many newspaper articles. You might enjoy reading her book *The Easter Pig,* a clever picture-book fantasy with a starry-eyed hero.

Illustrator

Rosekrans Hoffman is a painter as well as a children's book illustrator. Her paintings have been shown in several art museums. Ms. Hoffman has also written and illustrated several children's books. Among these books are *Anna Banana* and *Sister Sweet Ella.* Her illustrations in *My Mother Sends Her Wisdom* have been highly praised.

Selection Wrap-up

Summary Questions

At the beginning of the tale, Widow Petrovna owed Old Boris money. At the end, he owed *her* money. Use the questions to tell how this happened.

1. Why did Widow Petrovna owe Old Boris money? How did she pay him?
2. Why did Old Boris end up owing Widow Petrovna money?
3. Do you think the judge made a fair decision? Why or why not?
4. Explain Widow Petrovna's plan the way she might explain it.

The Reading and Writing Connection

What will Old Boris do next? Read these things that he might say when he leaves court.

I will be even more greedy.

I won't collect money from the other peasants.

I have learned my lesson, and I won't charge high interest anymore.

Which of these things do you think Old Boris would say? Write a paragraph that tells why you think he would say it. Try to use some words from the box.

wisdom	accounts	owe	fortune
debt	judge	wit	worry

Magazine Wrap-up

Story Characters

Think about three of the main characters from this magazine: Gretchen from "The White Stallion," Finn from "Finn McCool," and Widow Petrovna from "My Mother Sends Her Wisdom." Each character had a problem that was finally solved.

For each character, tell what the problem was and how it was solved.

Vocabulary

Look at these three categories: **Horses, Detectives,** and **Places**. Decide which of the words below belong in each category.

mystery	**meadow**
hoofbeats	**evidence**
plains	**riverbank**
agency	**mare**
bodyguards	**stallion**
mustangs	**forest**
mountaintop	**galloped**

Write a few sentences using the words from one of the categories.

Using the Glossary

You know that context can help you learn the meaning of a word that you have never seen before. However, sometimes you will still need to use the glossary to find the exact meaning of a word. Read each sentence below.

1. Several **blossoms** fell from the tree.
2. She is a **champion** speller.
3. The rabbit tried to **escape.**
4. The **goslings** swam in the pond.
5. He caught a **minnow** in his net.

Number a paper from 1 to 5. Look up the meaning for each word in boldface type in the glossary. Then write a sentence of your own using each word.

Books to Enjoy

Hinny Winny Bunco
by Carol Greene

The gift of a fiddle brings a happy change to a young farmer.

Don't Be Mad, Ivy
by Christine McDonnell

Six short stories show that Ivy is always ready to try something new and make new friends.

Amy Goes Fishing
by Jean Marzolla

A girl and her father share a happy day of fishing.

The Long Way to a New Land
by Joan Sandin

Carl Erik and his family make a long journey by steamship in 1868 from their farm in Sweden to America.

Caravans

Magazine Two

123

Contents

Stories

Blue-Wings-Flying

by Elizabeth Willis DeHuff

**Blue-Wings-Flying has a new
baby sister. His family members
will gather to choose a name for the baby.
Who will name the baby? What will that name be?**

Most mornings the sunlight sent its shining fingers through the little window and awakened Blue-Wings-Flying. But this morning something else awakened him. He listened. "*A-laa, a-laa, a-laa,*" he heard. It was the cry of a tiny baby.

Blue-Wings-Flying wiggled out of his blanket and sat up. So-Oh (the Hopi word for *Grandmother*) was seated by the stove. Beside her was a basket of soft gray ashes. Gently she rubbed some ashes over the body of the tiny baby. Then she sprinkled the child with cornmeal. Tah-Tah (*Father*) was standing on a wooden chair, hanging up the baby's cradle.

Yu-Yu (*Mother*) was sitting on her rolled-up mattress. Blue-Wings-Flying ran to her, unable to ask the question.

"Yes," said Yu-Yu. "You have a baby sister."

The baby was wrapped in a blanket grown soft with much use. So-Oh handed the baby to Yu-Yu, who held her a moment for Blue-Wings-Flying to see. He touched the baby's face with his finger.

Suddenly Blue-Wings-Flying felt afraid. He thought of another baby, his little brother, who had died. He leaned over and asked, "Will this baby sister stay with us?"

"Yes, she will stay if she keeps well and happy and has a pretty name." Yu-Yu smiled.

"I will play with this little sister to make her happy," said Blue-Wings-Flying, "and I will find a pretty name for her Naming Day."

"Yes," said Yu-Yu. "So-Oh and Tah-Tah and your aunts and uncles and cousins will all be watching for the prettiest thing they see or feel on this day of her birth. Then on her Naming Day, the one who has the nicest idea will be the one to name her."

"That will be many names. How will we know the best one?" asked Blue-Wings-Flying.

"The one that we begin to call her, after we hear all of them, will be her name," said Yu-Yu.

"I will go and look until I find a beautiful name," said Blue-Wings-Flying.

Yu-Yu gave him a pat on the shoulder. "Now you must eat. Tah-Tah will be waiting. You must help him fill the water jars at the spring."

Blue-Wings-Flying slowly shook his head. "I don't want to go, Yu-Yu. I want to look for a pretty name."

"You don't have to look far away for a name," said Yu-Yu. "There are pretty things everywhere for an eye to see. Keep your eyes open. Thoughts and eyes work together. Have beautiful thoughts and you see beautiful things."

Tah-Tah came in and picked up the big water jar. "Come, my boy," he said. "The burro and I are waiting."

Blue-Wings-Flying went outside. Tah-Tah was tying the jar onto one end of the blanket on the burro's back. He had already tied So-Oh's jar on the other side.

"*Ar-ray*," Tah-Tah called to the burro. The jars swung back and forth as the burro headed up the steep path. The burro moved very quickly, and Blue-Wings-Flying followed at a half run. He frowned — there was no time to look for pretty things to name his baby sister.

Tah-Tah noticed and said, "Nothing will look pretty if you frown, my boy."

At one turn in the path, there was an opening in the high wall. At other times, Blue-Wings-Flying had seen blossoms of Indian paintbrush there. He stopped to look inside. As he did, Tah-Tah spoke.

"No need to look for flowers. They appear only when it rains, and no rain has come for many months. The flowering plants are dried up."

At the bottom of the hill, the burro went more slowly, eating dried grass here and there.

Blue-Wings-Flying sighed to himself. "I have kept my eyes open, and I am not frowning, but I cannot see a good name anywhere. Everyone will have a pretty name but me."

Suddenly the burro stopped, his eyes wide open with fright. He wheeled around and dashed away as fast as the bumping jars would let him go.

Tah-Tah and Blue-Wings-Flying looked to see what had alarmed the burro. It was a rattlesnake, winding itself into rings, one upon the other. Its lifted tail was shaking angrily. The rings on the tip of its tail rattled to warn them off.

Blue-Wings-Flying stood as if he had been turned into stone.

Tah-Tah whispered, so low that he could hardly be heard, "Don't move. Don't show that you are afraid. We must let the snake know that we are its brothers."

Blue-Wings-Flying could not help feeling afraid, but he stood very still. Not even his eyes moved from the rattlesnake. Tah-Tah stood very still beside him.

The snake closed its mouth, lowered its tail, and straightened its body. Then it slipped away into the rocks and was gone.

After a few moments, Blue-Wings-Flying sighed with relief. Tah-Tah went to get the burro.

"There are pretty marks on the rattlesnake," thought Blue-Wings-Flying, "but a snake name might frighten a child."

When they reached the spring, they untied the jars from the burro. Tah-Tah said, "So-Oh's jar is lighter than ours. It is made of better clay. Take it and fill it with water."

His arms almost reaching around the big jar, Blue-Wings-Flying walked carefully to the spring. He lowered the huge jar into the water. The jar was so big that it was hard for him to get a good hold on it. Suddenly — *clink* — the jar slipped from his hands and struck the stone wall. Blue-Wings-Flying caught the jar, but a piece broke off and disappeared into the spring.

For a moment, Blue-Wings-Flying could not move. His eyes filled with tears. So-Oh loved the jar; it had belonged to her own grandmother.

Then he tipped the jar to fill it with water. A ray of sunlight made a rainbow in the mist coming up from the spring. Blue-Wings-Flying looked at the rainbow, but he did not think about it. His thoughts were all about So-Oh and the sadness she would feel when she saw the broken jar.

Tah-Tah had turned away to save his son from greater shame. But now Tah-Tah lifted So-Oh's jar and carried it to the burro. He gave Blue-Wings-Flying the other jar to fill, to show his trust. Then Tah-Tah put his hand on the boy's head. "There will be other jars. Things that break do not last forever." Together they reloaded the burro and began to climb the steep path.

So-Oh was cooking pancakes when they reached home. Blue-Wings-Flying watched her slowly shake her head as Tah-Tah brought in the water jars.

Blue-Wings-Flying ran to her. "Your jar was heavy, So-Oh. It slipped and hit the spring wall."

So-Oh could not speak. She stood very still, looking at the broken jar. Finally she turned and went back to cooking pancakes. Blue-Wings-Flying knew she was sad. He knew, too, that she would not scold him. He would have felt better if she had.

Yu-Yu stood by the cradle, rocking the baby. Blue-Wings-Flying ran over to Yu-Yu. She whispered, "I will weave a big basket. We will trade it in the village for a new jar for So-Oh."

"But it will not be an *old* jar," said Blue-Wings-Flying, trying to keep back the tears.

"The jar will be old for your sister when she is old like So-Oh," Yu-Yu said, smiling. Blue-Wings-Flying felt a little better.

Suddenly he wondered what time it was. He went to the window and peeked out. It was time for the sun to set. Blue-Wings-Flying hurried outside.

As always, the shining ball of sunlight slipped down behind the mountaintops, pulling behind it a great blanket of colors. Watching the beautiful sunset, Blue-Wings-Flying felt that he had forgotten something — something important, something he should remember.

That night Blue-Wings-Flying lay awake wondering what the sunset had tried to tell him. Then a picture came into his mind. He saw again the spring and the broken jar filling with water. He saw it clearly, and all at once he had a name for his baby sister. He longed to say it aloud, once, just to hear how it sounded. But it was a secret to keep until it was his turn to name the baby. Blue-Wings-Flying closed his eyes, the picture still in his mind. Soon he was asleep.

The next morning, some of his aunts and uncles and cousins came to help get ready for the Naming Day. So-Oh was spreading corn batter over a hot, flat stone. Blue-Wings-Flying liked to watch her peel the thin-as-paper bread off the flat stone and fold it into long flat sticks.

Tah-Tah came in with many heavy bundles of food from the trading store. Blue-Wings-Flying helped him unload. When they had finished, Tah-Tah turned to the boy. "This house is getting too crowded now. You had better go out and play."

Blue-Wings-Flying went out to find his friends, but he did not go far away from his own house. When he saw more people coming from many directions, he ran to go inside with them.

As soon as everyone was seated on rolled-up mattresses and sheepskins, So-Oh got up. She held an ear of white corn. Touching the baby's head with the corn, she said, "I name you Pink-Clouds-in-the-morning."

Blue-Wings-Flying looked around. He saw most of the people smile and nod their heads. "They like that name," he thought.

Tah-Tah took the ear of corn. He touched the baby's head with it. "I name you Singing-Corn-Leaves-in-the-wind," he said. Blue-Wings-Flying remembered the soft sound of wind blowing through the cornstalks by the river. It was a nice sound.

Yu-Yu's cousin took the corn. "I name you Shining-Sun-on-a-bright-tin-can." A few visitors put their hands to their mouths to cover their smiles.

Another cousin said softly, "I name you Running-Chipmunk."

One by one, each person gave a name. Then it was the turn of Blue-Wings-Flying-in-the-sunlight. He was the last because he was the youngest.

Yu-Yu whispered, "Let the ear of corn touch like a butterfly." Blue-Wings-Flying nodded.

He touched the baby's head lightly and said, "I name you Rainbow-Mist-at-the-spring."

He looked shyly around the room. No one nodded. No one was smiling but Yu-Yu. So-Oh had a thoughtful frown on her face. Then they all stood up to eat. "Maybe they did not even hear my name," he thought.

Blue-Wings-Flying ate little. When the other children had finished, one of the girls said, "Come play." She pulled Blue-Wings-Flying by the arm and together they went outside, followed by the other children.

After a while, Blue-Wings-Flying slipped away. He wanted to be there to hear what the baby was being called.

Blue-Wings-Flying went into the house and saw that almost everyone had gone. So-Oh sat holding the baby. Yu-Yu came to take the baby, and as she lifted the tiny bundle, she said, "Come, little Rainbow-Mist. You must go back to your cradle."

So-Oh got up. "Good night, little Rainbow-Mist," she said.

In his happiness, Blue-Wings-Flying hugged himself and laughed out loud. He went to the cradle and touched his mother's arm. When she looked, he smiled and watched her smile back.

Blue-Wings-Flying peeked into the cradle and said softly, "Good night, little Rainbow-Mist."

Author

The story you have just read takes place on the Black Mesa in northern Arizona. The author, Elizabeth Willis DeHuff, lived and worked there with the Hopi Indians for over thirty years. She also taught in the Philippines. Before her death in 1982, Mrs. DeHuff had visited many faraway places, such as Egypt, India, and Hong Kong.

Selection Wrap-up

Summary Questions

Blue-Wings-Flying searched for a name for his sister. Use the following questions to tell how he thought of the name.

1. What name did Blue-Wings-Flying think of? What made him think of this name?

2. Do you think that his family liked the name that Blue-Wings-Flying chose? What makes you think that?

3. Why do you think Blue-Wings-Flying wanted to find a beautiful name for his sister?

4. When Rainbow-Mist grows up, she'll probably want to know how she got her name. What would Blue-Wings-Flying tell her about what he did and saw the day he thought of her name?

The Reading and Writing Connection

Pretend that you gave Blue-Wings-Flying-in-the-sunlight his name. Write him a letter that tells what happened on the day he was born that made you think of his name. Try to use some words from the box.

aunt	relief	cornstalks
burro	struck	rattlesnake
alarmed	swung	

You, whose day it is,
Make it beautiful.
Get out your rainbow colors,
So it will be beautiful.

Nootka Indian Song

Butterfly, butterfly, butterfly, butterfly,
Oh look, see it hovering among the flowers,
It is like a baby trying to walk
     and not knowing how to go . . .

Acoma Indian Song

143

Word History

Do you ever think about your name? In the story "Blue-Wings-Flying," it was very important to find a name for the baby. To Blue-Wings-Flying and his family, the name had a special meaning. Did you know that almost all names have a meaning? The meanings of some names seem hidden because they come from old words or words from another language, but they do have a meaning.

Do you know anyone named *Leo? Leo* means "lion" in Latin, a very old language. The first person named *Leo* was probably strong like a lion. Maybe you know someone named *George*. The name *George* means "farmer" in Greek, another very old language.

Last names have meanings, too. A smith is a "person who makes things." Can you guess how a person named *Gold-smith* got that name? Many years ago a person in that family may have made things from gold.

144

Many people were given names because of their jobs. Other people were given names because of where they lived. A person named *West* may have lived west of the village. A person named *Hill* probably lived in the hills.

You may not always understand the meaning of a name that comes from another language, but the meaning is there. The name *Taylor* comes from the word *tailor,* meaning a "person who makes clothes." Do you know any people named *Schneider* or *Snyder?* In the German language, these two names mean the same thing as the name *Taylor.*

If you would like to find out the meaning of your name, there are many books that can help you. It may take a little time to learn the meaning, but it is always fun to find out.

Meanings in a Glossary

You know that a **glossary** in the back of a book gives the meanings of some of the words that are used in that book. A **dictionary** is a book that gives the meanings of many, many words.

The words that have meanings given are called **entry words**. Entry words are listed in alphabetical order. The **guide words** at the top of a page show the first and last entry words on that page.

For example, if you were looking up the word *drift* you might see these guide words at the top of the page:

crate/enjoy

You know that you would look for the word *drift* on that page because the word *drift* comes in alphabetical order between *crate* and *enjoy.*

Now suppose you read the following sentence and then looked up the word that is in boldface type:

Even though she was only in the first **act,** Mary practiced very hard.

If you looked up the word *act* in a glossary, this is what you might see:

act   **1.** The doing of something: *She caught her cat in the act of spilling the milk.* **2.** One of the parts of a play.

The entry word *act* is in boldface type. Sometimes more than one meaning is given for an entry word. Notice that there are two meanings given for this word and that each meaning has a number before it.

Sometimes after the meaning there is an example sentence. You can see an example sentence after the first meaning for *act.* This shows the entry word used in context. The example sentence helps you with the meaning of the word.

If more than one meaning is given for a word, read all the meanings. Then go back and read again the sentence in which you first saw the word. Use the dictionary or glossary meaning that best fits the context of that sentence.

After reading both meanings for *act* in the glossary, you would read again the sentence in which you first saw the word. If you tried both meanings that were given, you would decide that the second meaning makes more sense in that sentence.

Many words have more than one meaning. Here is the word *chat* used in two different sentences:

1. During recess, I had a **chat** with my friend.
2. As we talked, we saw a **chat** in a tree.

You probably know the right meaning for *chat* in sentence 1, but its meaning in sentence 2 might be new to you. If you looked up the word *chat* in a glossary, this is what you might see:

> **chat** **1.** A light, friendly talk. **2.** A North American songbird.

Now read sentence 2 again. Use the context for *chat* in that sentence to decide which glossary meaning is correct for sentence 2.

Choosing a Meaning

Use the glossary at the back of this book to help you get the right meaning for each word in boldface type. Decide which meaning goes best with the context of the sentence. Tell the entry meaning that goes with the context.

1. My mother works for a **company** on West Street.
2. Here are the **brushes** for painting the house.
3. The **current** carried the log downstream.
4. Near the big tree, the path **bends** to the right.
5. You will act in this **scene** in the play.

Can you use each boldface word in a sentence that shows the *other* meaning given for that word?

Skill Summary

- Entry words in a glossary or dictionary are listed in alphabetical order.
- The guide words at the top of the page show the first and last entry words on that page.
- Entry words are followed by one or more meanings and, sometimes, an example sentence.
- If there is more than one meaning, read all of them. Then reread the sentence in which you first found the new word and use the meaning that goes best with the context.

What's the Matter with Carruthers?

Part One   **by James Marshall**

Emily Pig and her friend Eugene notice that Carruthers, who is usually very pleasant, has become quite grumpy. What do Emily and Eugene decide to do to try to get Carruthers out of his bad mood?

One fall morning Emily Pig and her friend Eugene were taking a stroll in the park.

"What beautiful weather," said Emily. "I'm sure we are going to meet some of our friends here today."

"That would be very nice indeed," said Eugene. "It's such fun to bump into friends and have a little chat."

And sure enough, just around the bend, they came upon their old friend Carruthers, all bundled up in his muffler and overcoat. He was sitting alone on a wooden bench, gazing at the falling leaves.

"Good morning, Carruthers," they called out in their most cheerful voices.

"Good morning," said Carruthers, but his voice was far from cheerful. It was the kind of "good morning" that really means "Don't bother me. I want to be left alone."

"I'm worried about Carruthers," whispered Emily to Eugene. "He hasn't been himself lately. He's so grumpy and unpleasant."

"It's not like Carruthers to be unpleasant," Eugene whispered back. "He always has a kind word for everyone."

"Yesterday," said Emily, "I saw Carruthers do such a rude thing. You may find this hard to believe, but he actually stuck his tongue out at someone!"

Eugene was surprised. "It's not like Carruthers to be rude. He has always had such lovely manners."

"But that's not all," said Emily. "The children in the park are complaining. It seems that Carruthers took their ball away from them."

"Oh, no!" exclaimed Eugene. "I just can't understand it. It is certainly not like Carruthers to be mean. He has always been so fond of children."

Leaving Carruthers to sit alone on his bench and gaze at the falling leaves, Emily and Eugene continued their stroll through the park.

"There must be something that we can do to lift Carruthers' spirits," said Emily, "and we had better do it soon. If Carruthers continues to act the way he has been acting, he won't have any friends left."

"That's very true," said Eugene. "No one likes a grouch."

And so the two friends sat together on a large rock and thought long and hard.

"Well," Eugene began, after a long pause, "whenever I'm in a grouchy and unpleasant mood, I always listen to beautiful music. In no time at all I feel much better, and I'm sure that I'm much more pleasant to be around."

"That gives me an idea," said Emily. "Come with me."

Eugene wondered what Emily had in mind.

The two friends hurried home, but in a few minutes they were back in the park with their musical instruments. Emily was carrying her tuba, and Eugene had his tambourine.

"What a good idea," said Eugene. "When Carruthers hears our beautiful music, he'll be his old friendly self again. I'm sure that he'll be very grateful."

Turning the bend, they saw Carruthers, still sitting in the same place, still gazing at the falling leaves. Ever so quietly, they tiptoed up behind him.

Placing the mouthpiece of her tuba to her lips, Emily puffed up her cheeks and began to play, softly at first and then quite loudly. Eugene tapped on his tambourine.

"Um-Pah Um-Pah Tap Tap. Um-Pah Um-Pah Tap Tap." It sounded something like that.

But Carruthers was not impressed. Instead of listening to the music, he put his paws to his ears and growled, "That is the most awful noise I have ever heard in my life!"

He promptly got up and walked away.

Emily Pig and Eugene looked at each other. "Maybe we should have practiced more," said Eugene.

"No," replied his friend, "some bears just don't and never will appreciate good music."

Emily set her tuba on the bench and sat down beside it. "Just because we could not improve Carruthers' mood with our music, does not mean that we should give up. We must think of another way."

"Yes," replied Eugene, "we must not give up."

So once again they thought long and hard.

"Whenever I am in a grumpy mood," said Emily, "I always have a little snack. I'm sure that a tasty snack would be just the thing for Carruthers. Maybe he hasn't been getting enough to eat lately. Why don't we invite him to lunch for honey cakes and tea? You know how fond bears are of honey cakes."

"What a clever idea," said Eugene. "Let's go to your house right away and send Carruthers an invitation to come to lunch."

Summary Questions

Carruthers was in a grumpy mood. Use these questions to tell how Emily and Eugene tried to cheer him up.

1. How did Emily and Eugene know that Carruthers was in a grumpy mood?
2. How did Emily and Eugene try to cheer Carruthers up? Why do you think they tried to cheer him up?
3. Emily and Eugene had two ideas for cheering Carruthers up. Tell about the first idea and whether it worked. Then tell about the second idea and whether you think it will work.

The Reading and Writing Connection

Think of some different ideas for cheering Carruthers up. Then write a paragraph about one of your ideas. Tell what your idea is and why you think it will work. Try to use some words from the box.

mood	**rude**	**grouch**	**appreciate**
awful	**pause**	**actually**	**impressed**

What's the Matter with Carruthers?

Part Two   **by James Marshall**

**Carruthers continues to be rude and grouchy,
even after Eugene and Emily have played
their music for him. What is making
Carruthers so grumpy?**

Carruthers was in an even grouchier mood when he came home from the park and found the invitation to lunch waiting for him. Certainly he was in no mood to go visiting — but what bear can turn down honey cakes? So of course he went.

At Emily's house Carruthers was given the very best chair. Emily poured the tea and Eugene brought out the honey cakes.

"It's another beautiful day, isn't it?" said Emily, trying to start a friendly conversation.

"Not really," said Carruthers.

"You must enjoy strolling in the park," said Eugene.

"Not especially," said Carruthers.

"Your fur looks lovely today," said Emily.

"I've never cared for it," said Carruthers.

Emily and Eugene didn't know what else to say — Carruthers was so determined to be unpleasant. And so the tea party continued in silence, except for the sound of Carruthers munching on honey cakes and sipping tea.

When the cake plate and the teapot were both empty, Eugene tried again. "Well, Carruthers, you certainly must like Emily's honey cakes. You've eaten all twelve dozen of them."

"They were very tasty," said Carruthers. "Thank you for inviting me. I must leave now. Stuffy in here."

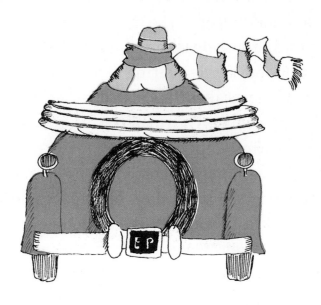

"Yes, it is stuffy," said Emily. "Why don't we all go for a walk in the fresh air?"

"I don't like walking," said Carruthers.

"Then why don't we all go for a drive?" said Eugene.

"A splendid idea!" exclaimed Emily. "I'm sure a change of scene will do wonders for Carruthers."

Before Carruthers could say anything at all, he found himself all bundled up again and sitting in the back seat of Emily's traveling car.

Very soon the three friends were sailing through the open countryside.

"There's nothing like a drive in the country to cheer the spirits," called out Eugene.

"The countryside gives me hay fever," was all Carruthers would say.

Not far down the road they passed a large sign.

"Ah," said Emily.

"Ah," said Eugene.

"Ugh," said Carruthers, "I hate amusement parks."

But Emily and Eugene paid no attention, no attention at all. "Rides and games are just what Carruthers needs," whispered Eugene.

"Yes," said Emily. "We are going, and that is that."

When they got to the park, Carruthers asked to stay in the car, but Emily would have none of that. "Nonsense, Carruthers, you must not be a bad sport."

Carruthers had never been very good at arguing, especially with Emily, and so he went into the amusement park. He rode all the rides and played all the games that Emily told him to play, but nothing seemed to improve his mood. He didn't smile even once — not even on the Ferris wheel, which had always been his favorite ride. He grumbled all through the fun house. And even after Carruthers had won several lovely prizes, he was still the grouch he had been all day. "I think it's time to go home," he said. "I'm not having a good time."

Emily and Eugene were so discouraged. "I was sure this would work," said Emily. "It seems to me that we have tried just about everything, and Carruthers hasn't improved one little bit."

"Yes," said Eugene, "I suppose there is nothing to do but take Carruthers home."

On the way home no one spoke.

When they pulled up in front of Carruthers' little house, Emily had one last idea. "Just look at all those leaves in your front yard, Carruthers," she said. "What a messy housekeeper you are. I really think we should help you rake some of them up before evening."

Now this was an idea that Carruthers did not like at all. Raking leaves in the late afternoon was not exactly his idea of fun, but he knew Emily was going to have her way again. So he went off to find three rakes and a basket.

"I don't see why we should help Carruthers rake his leaves," said Eugene to Emily, "after all we have done for him today."

But Emily had made up her mind. "Sometimes keeping very busy is a good way to get out of a grumpy mood," she explained.

"Well, we might as well give it a try," sighed Eugene.

When Carruthers returned, the three leaf rakers set to work. Emily and Carruthers raked leaves into the basket, and Eugene emptied the contents into a pile he had started.

Very soon the pile was quite high.

"If we hurry," said Emily, "we will be finished in time for supper," but Carruthers was already beginning to slow down.

He started to yawn — a small yawn, which he covered with his paw, to be polite. Then a much bigger yawn. But then — a great big bear yawn.

Without a word of warning, Carruthers plopped headfirst into the huge pile of leaves.

"What in the world has happened?" cried Eugene.

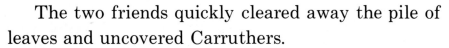

The two friends quickly cleared away the pile of leaves and uncovered Carruthers.

"He's asleep!" they exclaimed.

"So that is why Carruthers has been such an awful grouch lately," said Emily. "Why didn't we think of this before? He forgot that it was time for his long winter's sleep."

"Of course," said Eugene. "Carruthers should have been tucked away in bed several days ago. No wonder he has been so impossible to be around."

"There is no use waking him now," said Emily. "He'll be asleep for the rest of the winter. It's up to us to get him into bed."

"That will be the hardest job yet," said Eugene.

After a lot of huffing and puffing they managed to lift the sleeping Carruthers, who was just beginning to snore, into a small wagon and pull it into the house.

When they got to Carruthers' bedroom, they huffed and puffed again and, ever so slowly, they put Carruthers under the heavy winter covers. Emily pulled his nightcap down around his ears. Eugene set the alarm clock for spring and drew the shades.

"Good night, Carruthers," whispered Emily, giving him a kiss on the cheek. "Sleep tight, and we'll see you in the spring when you will be your old sweet self again."

Author

James Marshall is well known as a writer and illustrator of animal stories. His first book, *George and Martha*, became so popular that he wrote several more books about the two hippos. Friendship is a favorite theme in Mr. Marshall's writing. Emily and Eugene, the friends you just read about, appear again in *Yummers!* and in *Taking Care of Carruthers*.

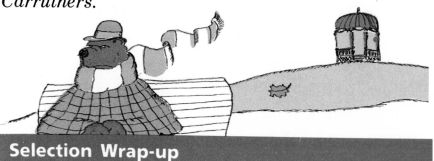

Selection Wrap-up

Summary Questions

Emily and Eugene did many things to try to help Carruthers. Use these questions to tell what they tried and what finally worked.

1. How did Eugene and Emily try to help Carruthers?
2. What finally worked? Why do you think it worked when nothing else did?
3. Do you think Carruthers will be grumpy again next fall? Tell why or why not.

The Reading and Writing Connection

Think about the ways Emily and Eugene tried to cheer up Carruthers. What do you think he would have liked doing best if he was in a good mood? Write a paragraph that tells what he would have liked doing and why he would have liked doing it. Try to use some words from the box.

splendid	**amusement**	**determined**
dozen	**conversation**	**impossible**
snore	**polite**	

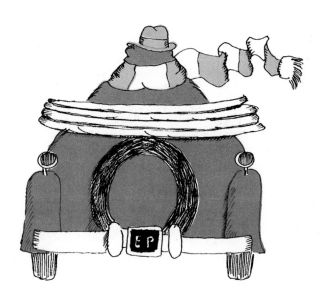

Winter Bear

by Karla Kuskin

Look at the snow.
Oh, look at the snow.
Ho, look at the snow come down,
As I sit here snug in my whiskered rug
Furry and warm and brown;
Scarcely asleep,
Hardly awake,
One eye open to watch a flake
Floating in flurries
Whirl swirlingly down
Touching the crest of the cold cream ground.

Who
Where
Is as warm as a bear in a storm
In the heart of a cave well chosen,
Covered by sleep
In the leaf-littered deep
While the world outside is frozen?

Multiple Meanings

In the picture, Emily and Eugene have different ideas about what the word *muffler* means. A *muffler* can be something you wear around your neck. It can also be something that helps make the sounds from a car quieter. The word *muffler* has more than one meaning. Which meaning is Emily using?

When you read, you will find many words with more than one meaning. If you read a word that does not seem to go with a sentence, stop and ask yourself: Does this word have another meaning? Then use other words in the sentence as clues to find the new meaning of the word.

Look at the pictures on page 173. Choose the sentence that tells about the picture. Then on a piece of paper, draw a picture that shows the meaning of the other sentence.

1. a. The horseshoe is made of **iron.**
   b. I will **iron** this cloth.

2. a. Eugene likes many **types** of plants.
   b. Eugene **types** a letter to a friend.

3. a. Emily pulls the **covers** up to Carruthers' neck.
   b. Emily **covers** her ears when it is cold.

Something Extra

Play a word game with a friend. Look through the story "What's the Matter with Carruthers?" to find as many words as you can with more than one meaning. You can look through Part 1 and your friend can look through Part 2. Write each word on a card. Take turns holding up the cards. Ask your friend to make up two sentences using the word you hold up. Tell your friend to use a different meaning of the word in each sentence.

Moose Baby

by Berniece Freschet

Have you ever seen
a moose? What is a
moose like? What are
some of the things that
a baby moose
might have to learn?

It was May. The morning sun shone brightly, and the air smelled sweet. Hidden in the tall marsh grasses, a wild goose sat on a nest of eggs. Close by, a gander stood guard, his long neck held high.

At the edge of the marsh, a moose lifted her head out of the water. Long ribbons of water weeds hung down from her ears. The big moose came out of the water. Following close behind was her little calf, Moose Baby.

Moose Baby had big feet and a big head, and he moved awkwardly. When he ran, his long stick-legs got in his way, and he would trip and fall.

His reddish-brown fur coat was much lighter than his mother's, and he did not have a hump on his shoulders, like his mother. When he was older, he would grow one.

Discovering

Early one morning, Moose Baby stood by the marsh. He watched for a while as his mother ducked her head under the water looking for plant roots to eat, but soon Moose Baby felt like playing. He jumped over a rock and went to look for someone to play with.

He saw small fish swimming in the marsh nearby. He waded into the water, but the fish swam away.

A beaver swam to the bank, pushed out of the water, and went over to a tree. With his sharp, orange teeth, the beaver chewed on the tree.

Maybe the beaver would like to play. Moose Baby came close, but the beaver did not even lift his head. He kept right on chewing. He was cutting down trees for the dam he must build. The busy beaver had no time for Moose Baby.

A small brown mouse popped out of a hole and stopped to eat weed seeds. Moose Baby moved near her and put his head down for a closer look. He sniffed, and the mouse ran and hid under a bush.

Moose Baby moved on. He came to a family of skunks. The mother skunk was digging under a log. She knew that under the log she would find some fat juicy bugs. Soon the baby skunks began to dig, too, and Moose Baby moved nearer to them.

The mother skunk was afraid for her babies. Was this huge animal an enemy? She raised her tail high and beat her feet on the ground, warning the moose to go away.

Moose Baby did not know about the warning. He came closer and closer. Suddenly his nose was filled with a terrible smell. The smell was so bad that he ran as fast as he could and splashed into the marsh waters. He stayed in the water for a very long time. Now Moose Baby knew:

Skunks do not make good playmates.

The Gray Shadow

One night Moose Baby heard a strange, wild sound. It was a coyote howling at the moon. Moose Baby was afraid. Maybe he sensed that the coyote was an enemy, or maybe he felt that his mother was afraid, too.

The sky grew light, and the howling stopped. The mother moose was even more afraid now. Moose Baby saw a gray shadow creeping close. He saw yellow eyes and sharp teeth. Moose Baby was afraid and began to run.

He ran faster than he had ever run before. This time he did not trip and fall. Moose Baby raised his head. *Whack!* A tree branch hit him right on his nose and hurt him. He stopped running and looked for his mother.

The gray shadow crept close again. Suddenly, the coyote ran to attack.

Moose Baby's mother came running. She leaped high and kicked the coyote with her sharp hooves. She kept kicking and splashing. Finally the coyote gave up and ran away to the hills.

Now that the coyote had seen the little moose, he would probably be back. It was no longer safe in the marsh.

The Long Swim

Every day the mother moose took her calf for a swim. Moose Baby liked to swim. Sometimes he saw the wild geese swimming with their goslings. Sometimes he saw the beaver working on his dam.

Today, Moose Baby and his mother swam much farther than before. Soon they were far out into a large lake. They swam toward an island, where the little moose would be safe from the coyote. Moose Baby was a good swimmer, but it was a long way to the island.

After a while he began to tire. Moose Baby put one of his legs over his mother's back, and he rested his head on her neck. When he felt strong again, Moose Baby swam the rest of the way by himself.

Finally they reached the island. For the first time, Moose Baby saw other young calves. Now he had someone to play with. The calves swam and raced together. They butted bushes with their heads in case an enemy was hiding nearby.

It was a happy time for the young moose. On hot afternoons, the moose herd rested together in the shade of the trees.

When the flies and other insects began to bite, the moose went for a swim or rolled in the mud. The thick mud helped protect them from the heat and from the stinging bites of the insects.

The island was a good place for a young moose to grow and learn.

Back to the Marsh

As the days passed, Moose Baby's fur coat grew darker. The hump on his shoulders began to grow.

One day the leaves on the trees began to turn red and yellow. It was time for the moose to return to the marsh. They waded into the water and swam away from the island. This time Moose Baby swam all the way back to the marsh by himself.

The days grew colder, and winter was on its way. Cold winds blew, hitting Moose Baby on his face and whistling in his ears. Soon the snow would pile into deep drifts, and food would be hard to find.

The mother moose would teach her youngster how to find food, and how to stay warm through the long, cold winter.

Next spring, when the new calves were born, Moose Baby would be big enough to be on his own.

Author

As Berniece Freschet grew up, she learned to love the outdoors. She has written a number of books, all of them nature stories. She carefully watches each of the animals she writes about. Several of her books have been chosen as outstanding science books: *Bear Mouse, Grizzly Bear, Year on Muskrat Marsh,* and *The Web in the Grass,* a book about spiders.

Selection Wrap-up

Summary Questions

Think about how Moose Baby grew and what he learned. Use these questions to tell what he learned.

1. What did Moose Baby learn in the marsh?
2. What do you think Moose Baby learned on the island?
3. Why do you think the island was a good place for a young moose to learn and grow?
4. At the end of the story, Moose Baby is back in the marsh. Tell how he could help a new calf.

The Reading and Writing Connection

Moose Baby saw a fish, a beaver, a mouse, a skunk, and a coyote. Choose one of these animals. Tell what happened when Moose Baby and the animal met. Tell what they might have thought about each other.

Make your paragraph a riddle. Don't tell what animal you are writing about. Let a friend guess! Try to use some words from the box.

attack	calf	creeping
splashed	hooves	protect
crept	marsh	

Survey

When you study an article or a chapter in a book, you want to understand the information and remember as much of it as you can. To help you to understand what you read and to remember ideas, you need to think about *how* to study.

This lesson will show you how to get ready to read and help you to use your study time better.

When you study an article or a chapter in a book, you should **survey** the article or chapter before you read it. *Survey* means "to look over." When you "look over" an article or a chapter, you begin to think about what information you might find when you read.

Do not take a lot of time when you make a survey. Just get a quick idea of what the information is about.

Title

The first thing to do when you make a survey is to read the **title**, or name, of the article or chapter. The title gives you an idea of what you will be learning. When you read the title, you begin to think about some of the things you already know about the subject.

Pictures

Next, look at the **pictures** in the article or chapter you are reading. The pictures may be paintings, drawings, or photographs. As you survey the pictures, think about some of the things you might learn.

Picture Captions

The words under or beside the picture are called a **caption**. The caption tells something about the picture. You should read the captions when you make a survey.

Headings

Some articles and chapters may have **headings**. Headings are words that are printed in boldface type between paragraphs or groups of paragraphs. The headings tell you what you will read about in each part of the article or chapter.

After you have made your survey, you are ready to return to the beginning of the article or chapter to read it carefully. Making a survey helps you to think about what you are going to learn. As you read, you should be able to understand the information and remember it better.

Make a survey of the article below. Then answer the questions that follow it.

Different Kinds of Bears

Bears are large animals with heavy fur. Some bears are black, some are brown, and others are white. Most bears sleep in the winter. Bears can appear to be friendly, but they can also be very dangerous. There are several different kinds of bears.

Black bear in western woods

Black Bears

Black bears live in the woods of North America. These bears are not always all black. Some have brown noses and white fur on their chest. Black bears sometimes come close to houses or camps if food is not put away carefully.

Grizzly Bears

Grizzly bears are large bears that live in western North America. They have gray hair growing in their brown fur, which makes them look grizzled. The word *grizzly* means "flecked with gray." These bears may be the most dangerous animals in North America.

Polar Bears

Polar bears have heavy white fur. They live where it is very cold and there is much ice and snow. Blending in with their surroundings helps protect these bears when they are hunting for food. Polar bears are good swimmers and get much of their food from the sea.

North American Grizzly bear

Polar bear in Arctic Region

Questions

1. What did the title tell you?
2. What kinds of bears will you learn about?
3. What did you learn from the pictures and captions?
   Now read the article.

Skill Summary

- *Survey* means "to look over" what you are going to read before you read it.
- The title, pictures, picture captions, and headings are things you should survey.
- A survey helps you get ready to read so that you will understand and remember better what you read.

When Winter Comes

What is winter like where you live? Is winter cold and snowy? If so, you probably live in the northern part of our country.

For animals who live in the north, winter can be hard. How do these animals find food? How do they keep warm? How do they stay alive when winter comes?

Red squirrel eating one of the many nuts it has saved during the summer

Saving Food for Winter

In summer, squirrels can find lots of food, such as fruits, green plants, and small insects. Summer is easy for squirrels; it is a time to grow fat. In winter, however, food will be hard to find. Squirrels get ready for winter by saving nuts.

When nuts grow ripe, the squirrels look for all kinds of nuts. With their teeth, they cut nuts from trees and let them drop to the ground.

Gray squirrels bury their nuts. The gray squirrel digs a hole with its paws. It picks up a nut with its teeth and drops it into the hole. Then it covers the nut with earth. Each nut that a squirrel buries has its own hole, and each squirrel buries hundreds of nuts in the earth.

Above: **Beaver in wintertime chewing on piece of bark**

Left: **Beaver preparing for winter**

When winter comes, the squirrel makes a home in a tree. When it wants to eat, it climbs down, pushes away the snow, and digs up a nut. It has saved enough nuts to last until spring.

Beavers also save food for winter. They save tree branches and logs.

A family of beavers works together cutting down trees with their teeth and biting off the branches.

They get the branches and logs to their house in the middle of the pond by dragging, carrying, pushing, or rolling them there.

Then the beavers begin a food pile by anchoring the branches and logs under water near their homes. Soon the pile of wood reaches above the water.

In winter, ice covers the beavers' pond and snow covers their house.

When a beaver is hungry, it slips out of the house and swims under the ice. It grabs a branch from the food pile and carries it home. Then it nibbles at the bark, as though it were eating corn on the cob. That's all it eats while winter lasts.

Sleeping Through Winter

A woodchuck doesn't save food. It stops eating when winter comes and sleeps all winter long. Before winter comes, the woodchuck eats a lot. It stuffs itself with grass and becomes fat.

On the first cold day, the woodchuck squeezes through a tunnel in the earth that leads to an underground den with four or five compartments. The woodchuck goes to one compartment and closes it off with dirt. It wraps its tail around its head and falls asleep on a bed of grass.

The woodchuck sleeps so deeply that it almost seems dead. Its breathing slows down, and its body becomes cold and hard. If you touched the woodchuck, it wouldn't wake up. The woodchuck might seem dead, but it's really not. Its extra fat keeps it alive during its winter sleep. Its body uses the fat for food.

Woodchuck preparing for its winter rest

The woodchuck sleeps all winter long. Sleeping through winter is called *hibernation* (hy-ber-NAY-shun). The woodchuck goes for six months without eating. When it wakes in the spring and leaves its den, it is a very thin woodchuck, but it will soon fatten up as it finds plants to eat.

Bears also sleep in the winter, but not so deeply. They, too, get ready for their long winter sleep by eating a lot. They often sleep in caves. On warm winter days, they may wake up and go outside to look for something to eat. When it gets cold again, they go back to their caves and sleep some more.

Black bear in forest searching for something to eat

Red fox hunting for food

Close-up of meadow mouse getting ready for winter

Busy All Winter

Some animals sleep through the winter, but others stay busy. These animals know where to look for food when snow covers the ground. They know how to stay warm in cold winter weather.

A red fox hunts for its food. It hunts through fields and woods for rabbits and rodents. The fox sleeps in the snow with its nose under its tail. Its fur coat keeps it warm.

A meadow mouse hides from the fox. It builds a winter nest of dry grass. Snow falls and covers the nest. To find food, the mouse digs tunnels through the snow. It runs through the tunnels and looks for seeds and roots to eat.

Snowshoe rabbit in summer

Snowshoe rabbit as its coat is changing color

Snowshoe rabbit in winter

Rabbits eat bark and twigs in winter. They sleep under bushes or in burrows where they cannot be seen. The snowshoe rabbit has a special way of protecting itself; it changes color. This rabbit's summer coat is brown. Its winter coat, however, is snow-white.

Deer spend the winter together in herds, looking for food in the woods.

They eat the bark and twigs of trees, as far up as they can reach. They paw at the snow to find nuts and weeds. At night, they pack down the snow, with their hooves, to make their beds.

Deer change color, too. Their summer coats are brown. Their thick winter coats are grayish brown, like the winter woods. In the photograph on page 190, you can see how the deer has changed color so that it blends in with the colors of the trees in the woods.

Bull moose in woods foraging for food

Moose, the largest members of the deer family, also spend the winter in herds. They travel together through swamps and woods, where they can be protected from strong winds. They feed on twigs and young shoots of trees. The moose's long legs help them walk easily in deep snow.

Leaving Winter Behind

Winter is a hard time for birds in the north. They do not mind the cold weather because their feathers keep them warm. However, they do have a hard time getting enough to eat because the ground is often frozen.

Many birds cannot find enough food in winter. When the days grow shorter, they fly south. In the south, food is easy to find.

Geese making their journey south in V formation

Blue jay

Hairy woodpecker

Close-up of monarch butterfly

Some birds stay in the north all winter. Blue jays hunt for nuts in the snow. Woodpeckers cut into trees with their strong beaks. They dig under the bark and eat hibernating insects.

Robins fly to warm places, such as Florida. Snow geese travel in huge flocks from North America to their winter homes which may be as far south as Mexico. Ducks may also spend the winter in Mexico. In spring, these birds will fly north again. This is called *migration* (my-GRAY-shun). It means to move from one place to another at a certain time of year. When migrating, birds may fly for many hours or days without stopping.

Some insects also migrate. They join in large groups and fly south. Thousands of black-and-orange monarch butterflies may fly south together in the fall.

Monarch butterflies after migrating to Mexico

How do animals survive the winter? Some animals get ready for winter by saving food. Then, when winter comes, they have enough to eat. Some animals hibernate, or sleep through the long, cold winter. Other animals keep busy looking for food. Still others migrate. They leave their northern homes and go south, where it is warmer.

Selection Wrap-up

Summary Questions

1. Name four things animals can do when winter comes.

2. Why is it more difficult for most animals to survive in winter than at other times of the year?

3. Name one animal that stays busy all winter. Explain why it is able to do this.

Art Activity

Divide a large piece of unlined paper into three sections. In each section, write the name of an animal from "When Winter Comes." Draw a picture to show how that animal gets ready for winter. Then under each picture write some sentences to tell about how that animal gets ready for winter.

A GIFT FOR ALICIA

by Lorenca Consuelo Rosal
with Patricia Olivérez

Alicia and her grandmother are very good
friends. Find out what happens to the special
gift Grandmother gives Alicia.

"Hold very still now, Alicia," Grandmother said. "I don't want to stick you with these pins."

Alicia stood carefully on the stool. She imagined herself to be made out of stone as Grandmother pinned up the dress she would wear to her cousin's wedding. Alicia wondered if she would have to stand still like this during the wedding. She had never been a flower girl before and was really looking forward to it. "I'll never be able to wait until Saturday," she thought.

"There," Grandmother said as she put in the last pin. "Now, step down. Come and look in the mirror."

As they stood in front of the long bedroom mirror, Grandmother put her hands on Alicia's shoulders. "What do you think, Alicia?" she asked.

"Oh, Grandma! It's the most beautiful dress I've ever seen." She gave her grandmother a big hug. "Thank you! Thank you for making it for me."

"Tomorrow, I'll finish the dress so that it will be ready for the wedding on Saturday."

"Grandma," Alicia said as she stepped out of the dress. "What was your wedding like?"

"My wedding?" Grandmother said. "It was many years ago, but still I can remember it as if it were yesterday." She walked over to the bedroom closet, took down a lovely old box, and put it on the bed beside her. Then she took out an old brown and white photograph and showed it to Alicia.

"I wore a long dress of white lace," Grandmother said. "It had been my grandmother's wedding dress. And see how handsome your grandfather looked in his dark suit!" Alicia looked at the photograph more closely.

Grandmother reached into the box again and took out a tiny heart-shaped pillow with gold coins attached to it.

"What is that?" Alicia asked.

"That?" asked Grandmother. "It's my good luck pillow. It was given to me by the women who were in my wedding."

"And you still have it? After all these years?" Alicia asked, surprised.

"Yes, of course," Grandmother laughed. "I've taken very good care of it. In fact, I have something else in this box which I have had even longer than the little pillow. Look," Grandmother said. She took a red handkerchief from the box, and carefully unfolded it. Inside was a small gold bracelet.

"Oh, it's beautiful!" Alicia said admiringly.

"My mother gave me this bracelet on the morning of my eighth birthday," Grandmother explained. "I remember it well because that was the day I was a flower girl at my first wedding. Now it is your turn to be a flower girl at your first wedding, Alicia, and I want you to wear this bracelet."

Grandmother put the bracelet on Alicia's wrist. "The bracelet is yours now. Wear it proudly," Grandmother said.

"I will," said Alicia.

"Now, it's time for bed," said Grandmother. "You've got school tomorrow."

"May I wear the bracelet to bed?" Alicia asked.

"Yes, but until you are older, you may only wear the bracelet here in the house, except for special times, like your cousin's wedding. Do you promise?" asked Grandmother.

"Yes, Grandmother. I promise," Alicia said.

The first thing Alicia did when she awoke the next morning was to look down at her wrist. Yes, the bracelet was still there, shining in the morning sunlight. Alicia knew that she would have to take off the bracelet before going to school. She had promised her grandmother.

"But it's all right if I just wear it a little longer," Alicia thought. "Just during breakfast, and then I'll take it off before I leave for school."

Just then, Alicia looked at the clock. It was much later than she had thought. Quickly, she jumped out of bed and got washed and dressed.

"There's just enough time for breakfast," she thought, as she dashed into the kitchen. A few minutes later, she was out the door, hurrying down the block to school.

"Teresita! Wait up!" Alicia called to her friend who was walking down the street. She ran to catch up with Teresita. They walked into the school building together.

"We'd better hurry," Teresita said. "I think we're late."

The girls rushed into the coatroom. Suddenly, Alicia cried, "Oh, no!"

"What's wrong?" Teresita asked.

"I forgot to take off my bracelet," Alicia answered. "I was in such a hurry."

"What bracelet?" Teresita asked.

"Here, I'll show you," said Alicia as she held out her wrist to show Teresita the bracelet. She discovered the bracelet was gone. "Oh no! It's gone," Alicia cried. "I promised Grandma that I wouldn't wear the bracelet out of the house. I meant to take it off before I left for school, but I was in such a hurry, I forgot. And now the bracelet is lost! Oh, what will Grandma say?"

"What's the problem?" Mrs. Ruiz asked, as she walked into the coatroom. Alicia explained to her teacher what had happened.

"Don't worry, Alicia," Mrs. Ruiz said. "I'm sure we'll be able to find your missing bracelet. Perhaps it slipped off when you took off your coat. Let's look around."

Teresita and Mrs. Ruiz helped Alicia look for the bracelet.

"It's not on the floor," Teresita said.

"Did you check your sleeves?" asked Mrs. Ruiz.

"Yes, and my coat pockets, too, but the bracelet is gone," Alicia sighed.

"Alicia, why don't you and Teresita walk down the hall and look for it?" said Mrs. Ruiz. "It's all right if you're both a few minutes late."

"Don't worry," Teresita said to her friend. "We'll find it."

But Alicia was not so sure.

A few minutes later, Alicia and Teresita came back to the classroom. Mrs. Ruiz could tell by the look on Alicia's face that she had not found the bracelet.

"I'm so sorry," Mrs. Ruiz said, "but maybe it will turn up."

All day long Alicia had trouble thinking about her schoolwork, because all of her thoughts were on the lost bracelet and how upset her grandmother would be! That afternoon Alicia checked the coat-room again, but the bracelet was simply not there.

The walk home was long and slow. How could she ever face her grandmother? How could she tell her what had happened? How could she show her how sorry she was? Alicia felt that she had done something terrible and that perhaps her grand-mother would never trust her again.

Alicia slipped in the door of her house. She could hear Grandmother's footsteps down the hall.

"Alicia, you're home," Grandmother said. "How was your day at school?"

Alicia said nothing. She took off her coat and hung it in the closet. She looked down at the floor. Suddenly, her eyes filled with tears.

"Oh, Grandma!" Alicia cried as she ran into Grandmother's arms.

"Alicia. Tell me, why are you so upset?" Grand-mother said. She gently stroked Alicia's hair.

Then Alicia blurted out the whole story. "Oh, Grandma. I didn't mean to wear the bracelet to school. I forgot, and now it is gone. I've looked everywhere, but I can't find it. I know I don't have a good excuse, but I'm so sorry."

"I know you are, Alicia," Grandmother said, "but you are old enough now to take better care of things and to take responsibility for what you do. But come," Grandmother said cheerfully. "Dry your tears. I have something to show you."

Grandmother led Alicia into her bedroom. There, lying on the bed, was Alicia's new dress.

"I finished it for you today," Grandmother said.

"Thank you," Alicia said, but her voice still sounded very sad.

"I have something else to show you, too," Grandmother said. "Look."

Alicia, still sniffling, looked up. There, before her eyes, was the gold bracelet.

"Grandma! You have the bracelet? But how?" Alicia wondered.

"The bracelet must have slipped off when you were getting dressed this morning. I found it on the bedroom floor this afternoon when I brought in your new dress," Grandmother explained.

"But why didn't you tell me right away?" Alicia asked.

"It was important for you to tell me yourself, Alicia," Grandmother said. Then she handed the bracelet to her granddaughter.

"I'll put it someplace until tomorrow," Alicia promised. "I was so worried about the bracelet, I almost forgot about the wedding tomorrow morning. I'll wear a beautiful dress and a beautiful bracelet."

Then Alicia wrapped her arms around her grandmother and gave her a big hug.

Authors

Lorenca Consuelo Rosal was very fond of her grandmother, who taught her the meaning of responsibility, just as Alicia's grandmother did. Ms. Rosal has written many other stories for children and has also written stories for adults.

Patricia Olivérez is a librarian in Salinas, California, where she edits the young adults newsletter at the John Steinbeck Library. She has taught elementary and secondary school.

Summary Questions

Alicia learned about responsibility the hard way. Use these questions to tell how.

1. Why did Grandmother give Alicia her gold bracelet? Why was the bracelet special?
2. How do you think Alicia felt when she lost the bracelet? What makes you think that?
3. What happened when Alicia told Grandmother what she had done? Do you think Alicia did the right thing? Why or why not?
4. Pretend that Alicia is giving the gold bracelet to *her* granddaughter. Tell what Alicia might say about the bracelet and about the lesson she once learned.

The Reading and Writing Connection

The things shown below were in Grandmother's box:

Choose one of these things or something else you think Grandmother could have given to Alicia. Write a paragraph. Describe the thing, tell what you think Alicia will do with it, and tell why you think she will do this. Try to use some words from the box below.

gift	**simply**	**responsibility**
wrist	**attached**	**wedding**

Dragon Stew

**written by
Tom McGowen**

**illustrated by
Nick Harris**

The king in this story loves to eat. He also likes to give orders and advice to royal cooks while they are preparing meals. Now all of the royal cooks have quit and the king is searching for a new one.

At last he finds a perfect cook with an unusual recipe — dragon stew. The new cook has a foolproof plan to keep the king happy — until the king's soldiers bring in a small, fat dragon! This leads to some tricky problems that only the dragon can solve.

Dragon Stew

by Tom McGowen

illustrated by Nick Harris

Once upon a time, there was a kingdom ruled by a king who was so fond of food that he couldn't bear to be without it for very long.

Eating was his hobby. He began with a big breakfast at eight o'clock, had a light snack at ten, and a large lunch at twelve. Then he exercised by watching two tennis players, and since exercise gave him an appetite, he ate a small snack at about two in the afternoon.

At four o'clock, he had sandwiches and at seven in the evening he happily sat down to a royal banquet. There was one of these every evening, even if the king was the only one at the table.

Eating was so important to him that it affected everything he did, and sometimes it got him in trouble. For example, he was always losing his royal cooks. He just couldn't keep from telling them how to improve their cooking. He insisted on making changes in every dish. Since royal cooks are very proud, they resented this. Six cooks had already left in a huff.

One evening the king entered the banquet hall and saw a sandwich on his plate. He knew what had happened. "Oh, my," he sighed, "I see that royal cook number seven has left!"

"Yes, your Majesty," replied the head cook. "He said he could no longer cook for a king who kept changing all his recipes. And now there are no more royal cooks available! None of those you've had will ever come back, and all the others are cooking for other kings. I don't know how to find another cook. There just aren't any left!"

The king looked worried for a moment, then brightened. "I know! Royal cooks *are* royal cooks because they have the imagination to make up unusual recipes. There must be many good cooks with imagination in my kingdom. We'll have a contest, and the one who tells me the most unusual recipe can be the royal cook!"

The next day proclamations were posted throughout the kingdom inviting all cooks to enter the contest. There was great excitement. Cooks from all over the kingdom came clamoring to the castle.

They formed a line that began at the back of the castle, wound around to the front, crossed the drawbridge, entered the gate, jammed the courtyard, went up the stairs, and flowed into the throne room where the king was interviewing them. In they came, bowing, smiling hopefully, and offering enough recipes to fill seven huge cookbooks or seventy hungry kings.

To each, the king simply shook his head. "That's not unusual," he'd say, or "I've eaten that before."

While this was going on, a shabby young man came trudging up the road toward the castle. He had patched knees and elbows, and the feather in his worn hat was bedraggled. But he had a merry grin, and he was whistling a cheerful tune. When he saw the long line of people, he asked a soldier standing nearby, "What's going on? Why are all these people lined up around the castle?"

"The king's looking for a new royal cook," the soldier replied. "The cook with the most unusual recipe will get the job and will live in the palace off the best of the land!"

220

"Wouldn't that be wonderful!" said the young man.

"Well, I don't know," said the soldier. "Cooks don't get along with the king. He tells them what to do, puts things in their cooking pots — he all but does the cooking himself."

"You don't say?" said the young man, and he got into line.

"Oh, are you a cook?" asked the soldier.

"I'm just the sort of cook the king wants," he answered, "and I have the most unusual recipe he's ever heard of!"

It was late afternoon when the young man reached the throne room. The king was looking glum. Not one cook had offered him a recipe that he considered unusual. Now the last of them was this ragged fellow who looked far too thin to be much of a cook. "Well, what's your name and recipe?" the king asked.

"I'm Klaus Dinkelspiel, your Majesty. My recipe is so unusual, so rare, that I'm sure you've never heard of it. It's — dragon stew!"

The king gasped. "That sounds different. What's in it — besides a dragon, of course?"

"Oh, I can't tell you!" exclaimed Klaus. "It has been a secret in my family for over one hundred years."

"I understand," nodded the king, "but if we can ever locate a dragon, you must make it for me. However, you can begin preparing an ordinary royal banquet. You are the new royal cook."

Klaus bowed deeply. "Now, your Majesty, what would you like for dinner?" he asked.

"How about roast pig with applesauce?" asked the king.

"And would your Majesty care to show me exactly how you want it cooked?" Klaus asked innocently.

The king stared. "You mean you won't care if I offer advice and suggestions? Why, you and I are going to get along just fine!"

So off they went to the kitchen and collected everything the king needed. Then Klaus asked, "Now, how would you prepare this, your Majesty?"

The King, greatly delighted, stuffed the pig and then peeled and sliced the apples.

"How would you cook this, your Majesty?" asked Klaus.

The king happily popped the pig into the oven and then stirred the applesauce.

Klaus watched and kept saying, "That's just how I'd have done it."

When the pig was brown and juicy and the sauce was bubbling merrily, Klaus said, "I thank you for all your suggestions, your Majesty. If you will go to the banquet hall, I'll serve you the banquet I have prepared."

When the king had gobbled up the last piece of pork and the last drop of sauce, he announced that it was the finest banquet he'd ever eaten and that Klaus was the finest cook he'd ever had. From then on, the king and his new cook were quite pleased — the king because he now had all his favorite dishes cooked exactly as he liked them and Klaus because he was living off the best of the land.

One morning, a good many months after Klaus had become the royal cook, he was called to the throne room. When he entered, he was horrified to see the captain of the guard and a dozen scratched and smoke-blackened soldiers surrounding a large cage inside of which was a small, fat dragon.

"Surprise!" beamed the king. "I sent them out to find a dragon months ago, and it's taken all this time to find one. Now you can cook your special dragon stew tonight. I promise I won't try to find out your secret — I won't even set foot in the kitchen today!"

The soldiers carried the cage to the kitchen, set it down, and marched out. The captain said, "Careful of him, Cook. He bites, scratches, and breathes fire!"

Klaus stared at the small dragon. A tear trickled down his cheek. "Are you trying to think of the best way to kill me?" it asked, accusingly. "It isn't fair! I was minding my own business, bothering no one, and suddenly your soldiers captured me. They carried me here to be made into — into stew."

"Believe me, dragon," said Klaus, "I don't want to make you into stew. I didn't think there were any dragons when I made up that silly old recipe. I just wanted to fool the king into thinking I was a cook. I couldn't make any stew if my life depended on it — and it probably does. The king will be rid of me when he finds out that I fooled him."

"Oh, making stew is easy," said the dragon. "You soak the meat in vinegar, brown it in butter, and simmer it slowly in its own juice with onions and carrots. And then ..."

"You can cook?" asked Klaus. "I thought all dragons ever did was to breathe fire and frighten people."

"Nonsense!" said the dragon. "Living alone, I've had to do all my own cooking. I've become quite a splendid cook, if I do say so myself."

Suddenly, Klaus began to grin and nod his head as though he had thought of something.

At seven o'clock, the king hurried into the banquet hall, anxious to taste Klaus's wonderful dragon stew. He watched eagerly as Klaus carried in a steaming bowl and served chunks of beautifully browned meat and vegetables onto the king's plate. The king began to eat. After four helpings, he leaned back with a sigh.

"That certainly was one of the best stews I've ever eaten. What a shame we can never have it again. That was probably the world's last dragon."

"Oh, we can have it as often as you like, your Majesty," Klaus calmly announced. "You see, the thing that makes dragon stew such a rare recipe is that it can only be cooked *by* a dragon! Allow me to present my assistant."

Klaus whistled, and in came the dragon, wearing a tall, white cook's hat and a gravy-stained apron. The dragon bowed deeply.

"Under my direction," said Klaus with a grin, "my assistant will be happy to make dragon stew whenever you want it."

So everything turned out very well. The king was able to cook his own banquets just as he liked them. He could also have dragon stew (made from beef) as often as he wanted it. Klaus was happy to be living off the best of the land without having to work hard for it. The dragon was delighted to be an assistant royal cook.

But the happiest person of all was the kitchen helper. One of his jobs had been to light the fire in the big stove, often getting burned as he did it. Now he no longer had this task, for the assistant royal cook lit his own stove by breathing fire into it!

Author

Tom McGowen is a writer, an artist, and an editor. He has also had a variety of jobs in advertising. Mr. McGowen has written over twenty books for children. Some of them are humorous picture books like *Dragon Stew*, and others are books for older readers. His attractive science books, such as *Album of Dinosaurs* and *Album of Sharks*, are always well worn in libraries and are very popular. His book *Album of Whales* was chosen as an Outstanding Science Trade Book for Children in 1980.

Illustrator

Nick Harris, an English artist, was born in Hampshire on the south coast of England. He grew up and went to school in Gloucester. After studying art in London, Mr. Harris became an illustrator. His illustrations have appeared in a number of books and magazines. Among them are fairy tales and King Arthur legends.

Summary Questions

At first the king didn't have a cook. Later he had both a cook and an assistant cook. Use the questions to tell how this happened.

1. Why didn't the king have a royal cook at first?
2. How did Klaus get to be the royal cook? How did he keep the job?
3. Do you think Klaus was a good royal cook? Why or why not?
4. At the end of the story, the king, Klaus, the dragon, and the kitchen helper were all happy. Tell why each one was happy.

The Reading and Writing Connection

The king had proclamations posted to announce the cooking contest. Write a proclamation that announces the contest. Try to use some words from the box.

assistant	recipe	stew
banquet	appetite	anxious
royal	interviewing	ordinary

Magazine Wrap-up

Looking Back

Think about the stories you have read in this magazine:

"Blue-Wings-Flying"
"What's the Matter with Carruthers?"
"Moose Baby"
"A Gift for Alicia"
"Dragon Stew"

Which of these stories have animals in them? Name some of these animals.

In which stories are the animals as you would see them in real life? In which stories are they fanciful? Tell how these animals were important in the stories in which they appeared.

Vocabulary

Here are three characters from this magazine:

Blue-Wings-Flying
Carruthers
Moose Baby

Look at the words below. Decide which words belong with each character named above. Tell why.

marsh	**burro**
coyote	**calf**
rattlesnake	**rude**
grouchy	**cradle**
splashed	**snore**
cornstalks	**honey**

Glossary: Word Meaning

You know that many words have more than one meaning. When a glossary entry gives more than one meaning, read all of them. Then reread the sentence in which you first found the new word and use the meaning that goes best with the context.

Look at the sentences below. Look up the boldface words in the Glossary. Use the context to help you decide which meaning is correct in each sentence.

1. The baby took one **step** and then fell.
2. Mike's eyes were wide with **alarm** when he saw the storm cloud.
3. We watched the lovely **monarch** land on a plant.
4. We have a strawberry **patch** in our back yard.

Write a sentence of your own showing the *other* glossary meaning for each word.

Books To Enjoy

Blizzard at the Zoo
by Robert Bahr
The zookeepers care for the animals in the zoo during the worst blizzard Buffalo ever had.

The Best Town in the World by Byrd Baylor
Growing up in a small Texas town many years ago was very special. The best blackberries grew there, and even the dogs were smarter.

Lucky Porcupine
by Miriam Schlein
Here is a lively description of what porcupines are like and how they live.

A Chair for My Mother
by Vera B. Williams
After a fire in their home, a girl and her hard-working mother and grandmother save their money to buy a beautiful new soft armchair.

Caravans

Magazine Three

Contents

Stories

238

Benny's Flag

by Phyllis Krasilovsky

Benny is a boy who has many hopes and dreams. What might some of them be? Will some of his hopes and dreams come true?

Benny was a boy who lived in Alaska many years before it became a state. He had a happy, friendly smile. Everyone liked Benny, for Benny liked everyone. He had no father and mother, but he had many friends in the mission home where he lived. That was a place for children who had no families.

The children ate in a big dining room and slept in large rooms, called dormitories, that had many beds. They all went to the school in the village.

Benny was happy in the mission home, but sometimes before he went to sleep at night, he would gaze at the stars outside his dormitory window. He longed for the day when he would be a grown-up, for then he was going to be a fine fisherman. He would use a big net, like the Big Dipper in the sky, to catch splendid silver fish. Benny looked at the Great Bear, a larger group of stars of which the Big Dipper was a part. Like the great strong bear of night, Benny would be big and strong himself.

The North Star would guide his boat, for the North Star was the star of Alaska. Benny knew that when Alaska became a state someday, it would be the northernmost state in the United States.

Sometimes when the sky was scattered with hundreds of stars, it reminded Benny of a field of forget-me-nots, the little star-shaped flowers that grow wild everywhere. The blue sky was a roof that covered Benny's Alaska at night.

In the summertime, when only the mountaintops were still covered with snow, Benny enjoyed himself on picnics with the other mission children. Sometimes he went swimming, too, though the water was often quite cold.

One lucky day, a kind fisherman took Benny fishing with him in his boat. Almost at once, Benny caught a big silver salmon all by himself. It was so big that there was enough for everyone at the mission house to eat for supper, and everyone said it was delicious.

Benny was so happy he could hardly sleep that night. He lay awake looking at the stars, dreaming his dream of becoming a fine fisherman and owning his own boat one day.

When fall came, school started again. Then winter came quickly, far more quickly than it does anywhere else. The first snowy day Benny went to school wearing a parka, which is a fur-hooded jacket, and mukluks, which are fur-lined boots, and thick mittens to keep his fingers warm.

As he walked along the snow-covered road, he wondered if all the little blue forget-me-not flowers that covered the fields in summer were now growing under the earth. In the cold winter sunshine, the world was all white-and-twinkly snow. The silver fish had gone downstream to warmer places. The fishing boats, anchored near the beach, looked like a fleet of ghost ships.

That day in school the teacher told the children that a contest was being held to design a flag for Alaska. With all his heart, Benny wanted to win the contest. He thought how exciting it would be to see his flag carried in a parade, or hung on the flagpole at the mission house on holidays, or flown at the masts of big ships that came to the village in the summertime. He thought how especially fine it would be to see his flag flying on the fishing boat he would have one day.

That night the boys and girls at the mission house collected crayons, paints, and paper. They sat around a big table and made many, many designs for the flag. As they worked, they talked and laughed and sometimes held up their designs for the others to see, but Benny sat quietly, thinking and thinking. For once no one could see his happy, friendly smile. He was thinking of what he loved the most about Alaska.

Some of the children drew pictures of the beautiful snow-covered mountains in Alaska. Some drew pictures of the big fish that can be caught in Alaska. Some drew pictures of the northern lights that sometimes cross Alaskan skies.

Some drew pictures of the Alaskan forests, some drew pictures of the Alaskan glaciers, and some drew pictures of the Alaskan rivers. Several children drew star designs or stripe designs or flower designs.

Suddenly Benny knew what he wanted his flag to be like. He wanted his flag to be like the stars he dreamed by — gold stars spread out like the Big Dipper in the blue sky. So that is what he painted. Underneath his design, he wrote these words:

"The blue field is for the Alaskan sky and the for-get-me-not, an Alaskan flower. The North Star is for the future state of Alaska, the most northerly state of the Union. The Big Dipper is for the Great Bear — symbolizing strength."

245

Benny didn't show his paper to anyone. He was too shy. He thought the other children's designs were much better than his. Still, the next day he gave his paper to the teacher when she collected the others.

Several weeks went by, and the teacher didn't mention the contest again. Benny ice-skated, had snowball fights, and went sleigh riding with the other children. The winter seemed to go by quickly.

Suddenly the snow and ice began to melt. Benny no longer wore his parka and mukluks and mittens. He began to watch for the forget-me-nots in the drying fields as he walked to school.

He watched the fishermen mend their nets for the coming fishing season. He watched the world change from white to green.

Then, one day, when school was almost over, the teacher called the children together.

"Children," she said, "the flag contest has ended. From all over Alaska, boys and girls sent in designs for the flag. From northern Nome to the busy cities of Anchorage and Fairbanks ... from the fishing towns of Seward and Petersburg to Juneau, the capital, and the lumber town of Ketchikan ... from everywhere came hundreds of designs.

"And ... boys and girls! *Benny's* design has won the contest! From now on, *Benny's* design will be used on Alaska's flag!"

What a proud and happy boy Benny was! What an especially proud and happy boy he was on the Fourth of July, because on that day there was a big parade in the village. Everyone came to see the parade — to see the marchers in their bright uniforms, to see the baton twirlers. . . . But the very first thing they saw was BENNY . . . Benny marching at the head of the parade, carrying the flag he had made for the fishing boat he would have, carrying the flag he had designed for Alaska!

This is a true story about Benny Benson. He was a schoolboy in the town of Seward, Alaska, in October, 1926. Benny's design was chosen as Alaska's flag in May, 1927.

When Alaska became a state in 1959, Benny's design was used on the official state flag. At the time when Alaska was getting ready to become a state, Benny Benson was honored at a special meeting. Also, in the town of Kodiak, Alaska, a street has been named for him.

Author

Phyllis Krasilovsky has had a long and famous career as a writer for both children and adults. Many of her children's books have been translated into various foreign languages. For many years Mrs. Krasilovsky has traveled far and wide and has written articles and books about her experiences. One book that you might enjoy is *The Cow Who Fell in the Canal.*

Summary Questions

Benny loved the state of Alaska. Use these questions to tell why he loved Alaska.

1. What were some of the things that Benny loved about Alaska?
2. What did Benny want his flag to be like? Why did he want it to be like this?
3. How did Benny feel when he marched with his flag in the Fourth of July parade? Why do you think he felt this way?
4. In 1959, when Alaska became a state, a special meeting was held in Benny's honor. Tell how Benny might have answered these questions: *What was Alaska like when you were a boy? How did you get the idea for your flag?*

The Reading and Writing Connection

The children in Benny's class used different kinds of shapes in designing their flags. The bar graph on the next page shows some of the shapes that the other children used.

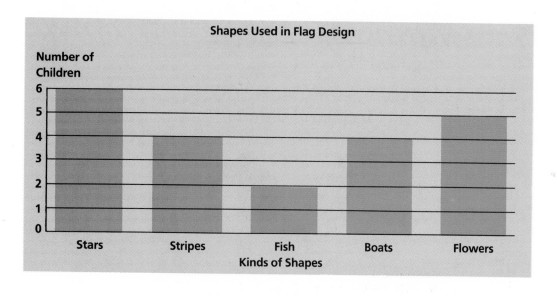

Shapes Used in Flag Design

Number of Children / Kinds of Shapes — Stars, Stripes, Fish, Boats, Flowers

Write a paragraph that tells about the children's ideas. Start with this sentence: *The children used different shapes to design their flags.* Answer the following questions in your paragraph:

1. How many children used flowers?
2. How many children used stripes?
3. What shape was used most?
4. What shape was used least?

Try to use some words from the box.

scattered	official	union	capital
glaciers	sleigh	future	state

251

The Skates of Uncle Richard
Part One
by Carol Fenner

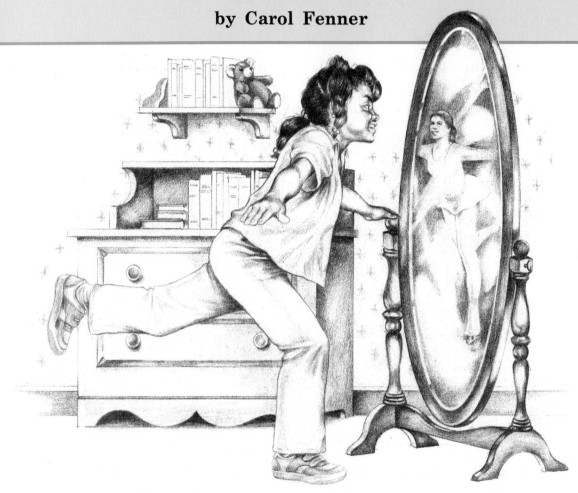

**Marsha has a dream of becoming a
champion ice skater. Will her dream
come true? Will she learn to skate?**

Once there was an ice-skating champion, a beautiful figure skater. She was tall and slender. She could swoop across the ice and leap into a double turn high in the air. She could spin so fast she could hardly be seen except for a whirling blur.

Her picture was in the paper on the sports page. Television cameras followed her around while she skated so that people could watch her at home.

Yet there was only one person who knew where she lived. A girl named Marsha knew — because the beautiful figure skater lived inside Marsha's head.

Marsha was almost nine years old. She dreamed of many things, but most of all, she dreamed of being a figure skater.

The ice skates of her dreams were snow-white with gleaming blades and little bells on the laces.

Marsha had been watching the championship skaters on television ever since she was six. A part of Marsha always skated with the skaters she watched. She learned the names of some of the jumps and turns the champions performed.

Marsha herself had never skated with real ice skates on real ice, although sometimes she skated without skates. She would stand alone in her room, her arms lifted in the empty air. She would bend forward and stretch one leg behind, but that was not nearly as exciting as being the champion skater who lived in her head.

The fall seemed to pass quickly, as Marsha was busy with going to school and playing with her friends. Still, she could hardly wait for the weather to become cold so that she could go skating.

Finally it began to get really chilly, and Marsha was looking forward to her birthday, in December. She began to hint to her parents that she would really like ice skates this year.

Marsha didn't think she would ever get ice skates for her birthday. Her parents always seemed to get her things they thought Marsha should have, not things Marsha really wanted.

Marsha worried a little, too, about what would happen to the beautiful skater in her head if the real Marsha ever put real ice skates on her real feet. Her dream skating, her leaps and spins, might not come true at all. Still she kept on hinting.

Gradually, whenever Marsha brought up the subject of ice skates, her mother would look thoughtful, and Marsha's hopes rose. Still she worried about losing the dream skater who lived in her head.

On the morning of her birthday, the first thing Marsha saw was her presents. Her eyes flew over the packages to a large box covered with red tissue. It had silver stars pasted into the shape of a big starry "M." Marsha's eyes brightened when she saw the red package, but she couldn't bring herself to opening it right away.

First she opened a flat box that contained a homemade sweater with red stripes. She unwrapped a new pair of warm mittens, two new books, and a paint set, but her mind was on the box covered with red tissue. Marsha's brother Leonard gave her a flashlight. Finally the present covered with red tissue was the only one left to be opened.

Marsha tore at the tissue, being careful not to rip into the big starry "M." When she finally opened the package, there inside the whispering tissue were the ugliest ice skates she had ever seen.

For a while, Marsha just sat staring at the skates. Then slowly she took them out of the box. They were old-fashioned hockey skates, black with brown leather around the thick toes, and brown circles at the ankles. They had heavy, blunt blades meant for stopping short and turning hard. Although the blades were clean and shining, it was easy to see that the skates had been used a great deal by someone else.

"They were your Uncle Richard's," said her mother. "They were his skates when he was seven. He was about your size then. He took good care of them, so they're almost good as new."

Marsha kept her eyes on the skates. She could feel her eyes fill with tears.

"Your Uncle Richard is a fine skater," her mother continued. "He learned how to skate on those skates. You can begin with those, Marsha, until we see how well you learn to skate."

Marsha sat on the floor with the ugly skates in her lap. "I remembered packing them away in the attic years ago," her mother continued. "Your Uncle Richard will be pleased to know that they're being used again."

Marsha was feeling the beautiful skating champion inside her head disappear. Her dream had left her, and the ugliest skates in the world were in her lap.

One Saturday morning, several weeks after her birthday, Marsha went to her closet, took out the ugly skates, and tried them on. They fit her fairly well. She stood up on them, but her ankles wobbled. She grabbed the edge of the bed, thinking, "I'm unsteady because there's no ice."

It was a cold day, but the sun was shining. "Today is perfect for skating," Leonard said. "Let's go skating after lunch." Marsha was excited at the thought of trying out her new skates.

When they reached the pond, there were many cars parked around it. All sizes of shoes and boots were scattered near the benches at the edge of the pond.

Marsha and Leonard sat on a cold bench to put on their skates. Leonard laced up his skates quickly. Then he stood up and waved to some friends who were skating on the pond. Leonard waited impatiently for Marsha to lace up her skates. "Hurry up, will you?" he said.

Marsha finally got her skates laced to the top and tied. She stood up. Her feet didn't feel as if they could fly across the ice. They felt like blocks of wood.

"Come on, Marsha," called Leonard. She took a step and the skates suddenly slipped away as if they were trying to escape from her feet. Up into the air went her legs. Down onto the ice went Marsha.

Leonard teased Marsha about her fall, but he helped her get up. From a distance, the frozen pond had looked smooth. Close up, Marsha could see that there were bumps and ripples in it, and some long, ragged cracks that had frozen over. Very carefully, Marsha stepped further out onto the ice.

Whooooooooosh! Up into the air went Uncle Richard's skates. Down again went Marsha! Leonard pulled her up by one arm, but her legs were going in different directions.

Whoooooooosh! Whoooooooosh! Down she went again. "Mar-sha!" complained Leonard. He helped her up again. "Now stand there," he said firmly.

Wobbling and swaying, Marsha tried her best to stay in one spot. Her arms were sticking out on either side, and her ankles were bent.

Leonard grabbed both of her hands. "Now," he instructed, "keep hold of my hands and keep your ankles straight." Then, awkwardly, he began to skate backwards, pulling Marsha forward. Her ankles caved in; her ankles bent out. Back and forth, in and out. She wobbled forward on the skates of Uncle Richard.

Marsha and Leonard weren't having very much fun. Leonard kept looking around for his friends. Marsha kept falling down. Finally Leonard pulled her to a bench and left her there. "I'll be right back," he said, and skated away to talk with his friends.

Selection Wrap-up

Summary Questions

Marsha wanted ice skates, but not the ones she got. Use these questions to tell why.

1. What kind of skates did Marsha want? Why?

2. How did Marsha feel about receiving Uncle Richard's hockey skates? Why do you think she felt this way?
3. What had Marsha hoped would happen when she got ice skates? What did happen?
4. Pretend that you are Marsha. Tell about your birthday. Then tell about the first time you used your birthday present.

The Reading and Writing Connection

Write a paragraph to complete Marsha's diary entry below.

Dear Diary,
    The first time I used my ice skates, I fell down a lot. I did not have much fun. Now it is two weeks later, and

Try to use some words from the box.

ankle	unsteady	swaying
wobbled	impatiently	instructed
gradually	swoop	

The Skates of Uncle Richard

Part Two

by Carol Fenner

**Marsha found that skating was much harder
on ice than it was in her dream. Will she
need to give up or change her dream?**

Marsha sat on the bench alone. She wanted to go home, but she didn't know how she'd ever get back across the ice to the bench where her boots sat.

Marsha looked up when she heard the scraping sound of ice skates stopping suddenly. A man was standing in front of her, smiling. At first she didn't recognize him. He was very tall and he had a long, red scarf that trailed over one shoulder. He was leaning toward her, saying something, and then she recognized her Uncle Richard.

"Marsha, is that you? Why are you looking so sad?" asked Uncle Richard. Marsha didn't know what to say. She saw that he was looking at her skates. "Why don't you lace up your skates properly?" he asked. He bent way over to look at them closely. Marsha could see that he was puzzled.

"They were your first skates when you were seven," she explained in a low voice.

Uncle Richard knelt down in front of her and took one of her feet in his hands. "Yes," he whispered. "They sure were ..." He looked up at her with delight. "Those good old skates."

He laughed and began to undo the laces. Marsha thought he was going to take the skates back. Then he said, "First, Marsha, you've got to have your skates laced properly. Your feet are falling out of these. They're laced up all wrong." Uncle Richard showed her how to lace her skates the right way.

"How does that feel?" he asked.

"That's much better," answered Marsha.

Then Uncle Richard helped Marsha stand up. He began to pull her slowly and evenly across the ice. "Bend your knees, not your middle," he told her. She did what he said and was surprised at how easily she could balance now.

After they had gone a short distance, Uncle Richard said, "You did that easily, so I will show you some things to practice while I do some skating." First he showed Marsha how to rest her ankles when they got tired. "Stand quietly," he said, "and let your ankles relax right down into your skates . . . right down into the ice. That's important."

Then he said, "Here's something else to practice. Watch closely." He pushed forward with one foot and trailed the other behind lightly without touching the ice. "Just bend your knee and lean into it," he said, "nice and easy."

Then he brought the other foot forward and pushed easily with that one. "I push," he said, "and then I glide . . . and then I push with the other foot. And then I glide! Push, glide . . . push, glide. Get it?" Marsha nodded.

"Now you practice that for a while. Okay?" Marsha nodded and Uncle Richard skated off, his red scarf trailing. She watched to see if he really could skate as well as her mother said.

At first Uncle Richard moved across the ice slowly. Marsha noticed that he glided a long time on one foot before he shifted his weight to the other one. Then he made some smooth, neat turns. His speed quickened, and he circled into a spin that blurred his entire outline. The red scarf whipped around him and, as the spin slowed down, the scarf gradually began to unwind.

"He really is a fine skater!" exclaimed Marsha. Her uncle began skating backwards. He seemed to be sailing. People began to stop skating to watch him. Suddenly he circled to a halt, skated backwards again, and disappeared around a bend in the little island in the middle of the pond.

Alone in the middle of the ice, Marsha took a few small steps. She skidded a little and then she glided a little. She stopped and rested.

Then she took a deep breath, bent her knees, and pushed off with her right foot the way Uncle Richard had done. She glided a little, her body balanced over her skating foot. Then she shifted and pushed with her left foot and glided a shaky distance. It worked! Push, glide . . . push, glide. She brought her legs together and glided on both feet all by herself in the middle of the ice.

She gasped with excitement. It was fun! She tried it again. She pushed off more boldly this time and glided farther. She did it over again. She practiced some more . . . push, glide . . . push, glide. She tried to keep her knees bent, her middle straight. Push, glide . . . push, glide.

Suddenly she realized she was at the other end of the pond. "My," said a voice behind her. "I thought I left you down at the other end." It was Uncle Richard. He was smiling. "How did you get here?" he asked.

"I push-glided," said Marsha. "All by myself. No one helped me."

"Are you fooling me?" asked Uncle Richard, smiling. "Let's see!"

Marsha skated in a medium-sized circle around him and stopped.

"You are one surprising young lady," said Uncle Richard. "You learn fast!" Marsha was surprised herself. "Are you ready for another suggestion?" he asked.

Marsha felt, in that moment, that Uncle Richard understood her better than anyone else. The beautiful figure skater of her dreams floated briefly into her mind, but Marsha didn't really have time to think about her now.

"I want to learn how to skate the way you skate," she said. Her voice sounded so little and low to her that she wondered if he'd heard her. But Uncle Richard looked very thoughtful for a minute. Then he said quietly, "Okay. We'll work on it."

He stood up. "First off, don't leave your body all bundled down inside your coat. Don't watch your feet. Stretch up. Be proud. Loosen up. Look where you're going. Reach after the sky . . . or the moon . . . or a treetop. Okay?" Marsha nodded, her heart pounding.

"You're a natural," said Uncle Richard. "You could be a very fine skater, but you'll have to set your mind to it."

Marsha nodded again. She understood. "Okay," she said, feeling sure of herself.

"Keep practicing," said Uncle Richard. "Next week we'll have another lesson. I'll talk to your momma." Marsha beamed at him. "They're a good old pair of skates."

Uncle Richard pushed off, and she watched him glide away. Marsha pushed off after him, her head riding high, her body stretched taller . . . reaching after him, after the sky or the moon or the tops of the trees. Push, glide . . . push, glide. She skated past her staring brother with hardly even a wobble. She glided away on the skates of Uncle Richard, feeling taller and taller, never once falling down.

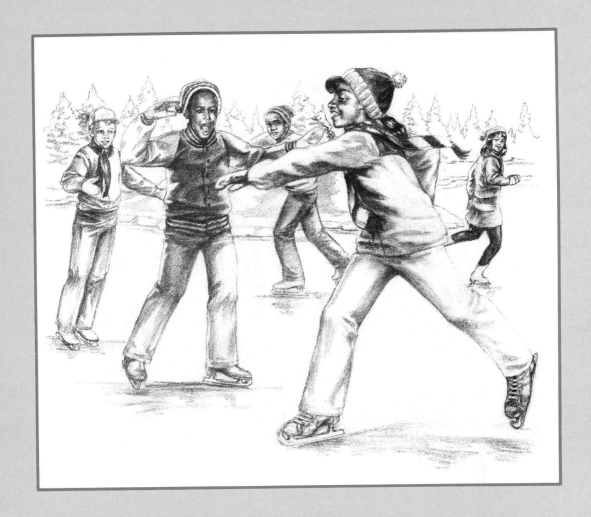

Author

Carol Fenner's books for children cover many different topics. Among them is *Gorilla, Gorilla*, an award-winning science book. The idea for *The Skates of Uncle Richard* came when she saw a small girl in hand-me-down skates being towed across an ice-covered pond.

Summary Questions

At first, Marsha couldn't stay up on her skates. Later she glided away. Use these questions to tell how this happened.

1. Why didn't Marsha give up when she kept falling? How did she learn to glide away?
2. Do you think Marsha will be a good skater? Why do you think this?
3. If Marsha wanted to help a friend learn to skate, what instructions might Marsha give her friend?

The Reading and Writing Connection

Imagine that you are watching skaters on a pond. Write a paragraph to tell about one thing that you see. Try to use some words from the box.

delight	**relax**	**shifted**
skidded	**natural**	**halt**
briefly	**scraping**	**recognize**
whipped	**entire**	**realized**

Dreams

by Langston Hughes

Hold fast to dreams
For if dreams die
Life is a broken-winged bird
That cannot fly.

Hold fast to dreams
For when dreams go
Life is a barren field
Frozen with snow.

Categorizing

You know that things can be grouped together because they are alike in some way. In what way are the things in the photographs below alike?

You could say that the things in the photographs are all alike because they are all *birds.* When you group things together like that, you are **categorizing** them. When you think about how things are alike, or how they fit together, you can make better sense of what you are reading.

Now look at the words below. Find the ones that name things that belong in this category: ***Clothing.***

pajamas	shoes	foot	shirt

Pajamas, shoes, and *shirt* are all clothing. *Foot* does not belong. It is not a piece of clothing.

Sometimes you can group, or categorize, things by what they *are*, like clothing or birds. Other times you can group things by what they *do*. For example, find the things listed in the box that belong in this category: **Things That Fly.**

bird	train	car
airplane	helicopter	butterfly

You would choose *bird, airplane, helicopter,* and *butterfly.* The other things do not fly.

Another important thing to know about categorizing is that things can belong to more than one group or category. For example, use the list again that is in the box on this page. This time, think of the things that belong in this category: **Things Used for Traveling.** Now you would choose *airplane, train, helicopter,* and *car.* So *airplanes* and *helicopters* can fly, and they are also used for traveling!

You can categorize *groups of words* and *sentences,* too. Find the groups of words below that could be listed under **Happy Children.**

smiling faces	tearful eyes
loud laughter	excited giggles

You know that the only words that don't belong are *tearful eyes.*

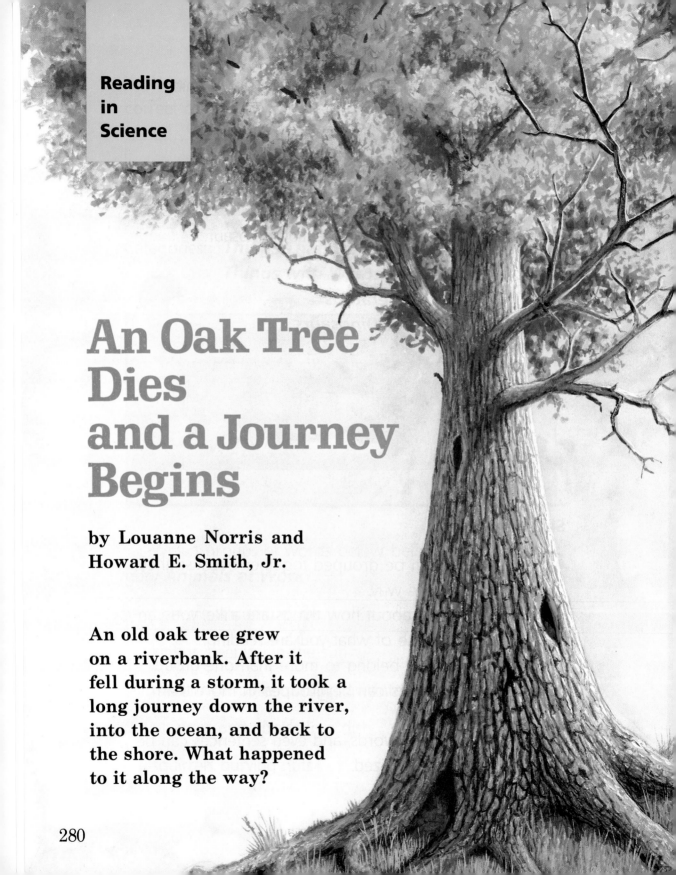

An Oak Tree Dies and a Journey Begins

by Louanne Norris and
Howard E. Smith, Jr.

An old oak tree grew
on a riverbank. After it
fell during a storm, it took a
long journey down the river,
into the ocean, and back to
the shore. What happened
to it along the way?

A big, old oak tree grew on the bank of a river. During the summer its green leaves hid many of its branches. Other branches were dead and bare. Light gray bark covered most of its trunk. Once the oak had had firm, pale brown wood under its bark, but over the years parts of it had rotted and turned gray. The tree had a few large holes in its trunk, and some of its branches had broken off.

Close-up of leaf and acorn from white oak tree

On the Riverbank

One autumn night, the biggest storm in years shook the old oak tree. Strong winds whipped away many of its yellow and brown leaves. The tree swayed and creaked, and the wind pulled at its roots. Some of the roots that were rotten broke, and the oak tree fell to the riverbank.

Oak tree on riverbank

All winter long, the oak tree lay on the bank. Its top branches lay in the river, and ice formed on them. Many twigs broke, and the rest of its leaves fell off.

Floating Downstream

In the spring, more rain than usual fell, and the river rose. It flooded and spilled over the bank. The water became so deep that the tree began to move. It floated downstream with the current.

The swift-flowing water carried the tree downstream past forests and farms. It pushed the tree into the sandy shore of a small island.

Tree floating downstream

On an Island

Once ashore on the small island, the racing water forced the tree's dead roots into the sand, and the roots held. The flood stopped, the water went down, and the tree stayed on the island.

Where the sun shone on the tree, the wet wood dried out. The bark split in many places, and most of it fell off. The wood turned gray and hard.

In the shaded areas near the ground, the wood was damp. Molds and mushrooms grew there, and sow bugs lived in the damp wood.

Raccoon in hole in tree

Not all of the tree was on land. Many of its upper branches were under the water. They turned very dark, but they did not rot.

In the dried-out part of the tree, a raccoon found a hole where it slept during the day. At night it went hunting along the river for frogs, fishes, and small birds.

Frogs swam in the still water near the tree, and they hopped up onto the branches. When black snakes crawled along the trunk of the tree, the frogs hopped back into the water.

Snake and frogs on trunk of tree

Minnows and sunfish swimming near tree

Minnows swam under the tree's branches, and larger fish also swam nearby. Sometimes big river bass hid in the dark shadows of the tree. When smaller fish swam by, the bass swam out and swallowed them.

Two children often sat on the tree and fished. They knew that bass hid among the branches, and from time to time, they caught one.

The oak tree lay on the small island for several years.

Floating Out to Sea

One spring heavy rains fell again, and the river flooded. The water became very deep and moved very fast. Soon water covered the island, and the tree floated away.

The tree moved downstream with the current. The river became wider, and other rivers poured into it. The tree passed factories, buildings, and bridges. Ships went by; their waves splashed the tree and rolled it over in the water.

Finally the tree floated out to sea. At sea the tree moved up and down on the waves.

Tree floating past factories and buildings on its way out to sea

On windy days, the waves were so big that the tree would ride to the top of a wave and then glide down the back of it with its roots pointed toward the sky. The waves broke and smashed at the tree and pushed it deep into the water, but it always came up.

On calm days, as the tree bobbed gently in the water, gulls and terns flew over it. Some of the birds landed on the tree and rested. They cleaned their feathers and turned their heads this way and that as they looked around.

Seagull resting on floating tree

Close-up of barnacles

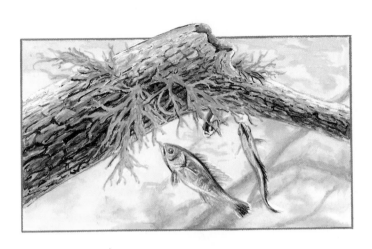

Sea bass nibbling on seaweed

Close-up of oysters and mussels

A few weeks later, bright green seaweed started to grow on the tree. Barnacles, mussels, and oysters attached themselves to the tree. Brown seaweed trailed in the water. Young sea bass swam under the tree. They ate the barnacles, mussels, and oysters, and nibbled on the seaweed.

Seawater soaked into the wood, and the wood became darker and softer. The tree was heavier, and it floated deeper in the ocean waters. All spring and most of the summer the tree drifted and rolled in the ocean.

Late in the summer a storm blew up. The wind blew very hard, and the waves became larger and larger. Huge waves crashed onto a rocky shore.

For two days and two nights, the waves battered the tree against the rocks. More branches and roots snapped off. The wood split; chunks of it fell off and drifted away. The rocks smoothed the wood. Almost all the seaweed, barnacles, and oysters were scraped off. After the storm, the tree no longer looked like a tree. It still had a few roots, but it was a battered log rolling in the water.

Waves battering oak tree against rocks

On the Beach

The log drifted close to shore. Some children at the beach pulled the log out of the water and onto the sand. They played on it, jumped over it, and built sand castles nearby.

Later, a very high tide carried the log farther up the beach. A strong wind helped push the log along and it became stuck in the sand.

Over the next few months, wind blew sand over a part of the log. Slowly the remaining barnacles dried out and fell off. The log began to dry out, and grass roots grew over parts of it.

Beetles crawled on the log. They gnawed little tunnels through the wood.

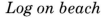

Log on beach

Log resting farther up beach

A rat built a nest under the log. At night the rat ate grass seeds and hunted on the beach for dead fish and other food. Then the rat scurried back to its nest. It poked its nose out, looked around, and popped back in again.

Beachcombers sawed off parts of the driftwood log for firewood, but part of a gnarled, bent root remained on the log. For over a year, sand blown by the wind had rubbed against the root, polishing it. In the sunlight it shone silvery gray.

One day a boy found the driftwood log on the beach. He broke off the dried-out root and held it up. He liked its twisted shape and its colors, so he took it home and put it on a shelf in his bedroom. Whenever he looked at it, he thought of the beach . . . and sometimes he wondered where the driftwood had come from and what had happened to it along the way.

A root of the oak tree

Authors

Louanne Norris and Howard E. Smith, Jr. are a husband-and-wife writing team. Together they have written books for adults and for children. Louanne Norris has been a social worker. Before Howard Smith became a full-time writer, he was a science editor. He also worked on "Mr. Wizard" TV science programs.

Selection Wrap-up

Summary Questions

The old oak tree traveled a long way. Use these questions to tell about its trip.

1. Where did the tree travel? How did it get to each place?

2. What plants and animals made a home in the oak tree?

3. Tell how the tree changed into the driftwood the boy found.

The Reading and Writing Connection

The following chart gives words that describe the tree when it was at different places. Study the chart.

Choose one of the places where the tree was. Write a paragraph that describes the tree while it was there. Use the words from the chart to help you. Try to use some words from the box, too.

ocean	gnawed
mussels	oysters
bass	polishing

On the Riverbank	On an Island	In the Ocean	At the Beach
yellow	split bark	dark wood	dried out wood
brown	molds	battered	gnarled
swayed	mushrooms	barnacles	bent
creaked			silvery gray

292

Windy Tree
by Aileen Fisher

Think of the muscles
a tall tree grows
in its leg, in its foot,
in its wide-spread toes —
not to tip over
and fall on its nose
when a wild wind hustles
and tussles and blows.

OLD BLUE

by Sibyl Hancock

Old Blue, the lead steer, is leading other longhorn cattle across the trail. Something happens during a storm. Davy has an idea. How will his idea help?

Before the railroads reached into the cattle country of Texas, the only way to move cattle was to drive them over trails.

One type of cattle was the longhorn. Longhorn cattle were the strongest and probably the smartest cattle ever bred. They could cross thousands of miles, and their hard hooves showed no wear.

Sometimes there was a special steer that was able to lead other cattle over trails. Old Blue was one such remarkable steer. He led cattle from Texas to Kansas for eight years.

As the story opens, Davy, his father, and several other cowboys are on a cattle drive in Texas. The story begins at dawn.

"Wake up, Davy!"

Davy opened his eyes. Cookie, the camp cook, was standing over him.

"I'll be right there," Davy said.

He pushed his blanket aside and folded it to make a bedroll. The cowboys sleeping around the campfire would soon wake up hungry for breakfast. The cowboys riding in from watching the cattle all night would be even hungrier.

A big longhorn steer with a hide so black it nearly looked blue lumbered up to Davy and nudged his hand. "Old Blue," Davy said softly, "are you hungry, too?"

Old Blue grunted and shook his
widespread horns.

Davy laughed. "You think you're better
than all those other longhorns. Who ever heard
of a big old steer sleeping around the campfire
with the cowboys!"

He patted Old Blue's shiny forehead. "You're the
smartest old steer I ever saw. Not many ranchers
own a steer who can lead all the rest of the cattle on
a trail drive."

Davy hurried over to the chuck wagon to help
Cookie. He was frying bacon in a black skillet over
the fire.

"Pa says I can ride today!" Davy exclaimed.

"Huh! Guess you'll feel like a real big shot!" Cookie said.

Davy smiled. He would be riding up front with the cowboys who guided the cattle over the trail. He knew that if Pa said it was okay for him to ride, then it was, because Pa was the trail boss.

"You're a lucky boy. Not many young people get a chance to go on a trail ride," Cookie told him.

"If Ma hadn't gone to take care of Aunt Clara's new baby, I could never have come along," Davy said.

"You can learn plenty on the trail," Cookie said, "but right now there's plenty to do here. Let's get to work!" Cookie handed Davy some tin plates to set out.

"Come and get it!" Cookie yelled.

While the cowboys crowded around the chuck wagon, Davy finished his breakfast. He took a handful of food scraps to Old Blue. The big steer was still eating biscuits and bacon scraps when Pa brought a horse for Davy to ride.

"Let's get moving," Pa said. "You watch what you're doing up there at the front with Old Blue."

"Yes, sir," Davy said.

"Feeling a little shaky?" Pa asked.

Davy nodded.

"I felt the same way on my first trail drive," Pa said. "You'll be fine."

Davy put on his hat. He climbed onto his horse and followed Old Blue up to the head of the herd. One of the cowboys gave the old Texas call, "Ho, cattle, ho, ho, ho, ho!" Soon the steers were strung into a line a mile long with Old Blue leading. There were over a thousand of them.

Davy watched Old Blue walk steadily to the north. No one understood how Old Blue knew directions as well as he did. Sometimes Old Blue walked too fast, and the lead cowboys had to slow him down.

"I don't like the looks of the sky," one of the cowboys said. "It could be a norther."

Davy shivered. A storm like that might bring icy weather, and they had a long way to go.

They had left the Goodnight Ranch in Palo Duro Canyon, Texas, a week ago. It would take two months to bring the herd into Dodge City, Kansas.

Davy guided his horse past tumbleweeds rolling slowly in the breeze. Sand crunched under hooves and rose in little gold clouds.

Cattle often tried to stop and eat dry clumps of grass. When they wandered into low trees, the cowboys had to drive them back to the herd.

Davy looked at the big steer. "Old Blue, you've got your work cut out for you. Here comes the river. We have to get across before the wind changes." The water was icy, but Old Blue plunged right into it. The cattle and the cowboys followed.

"Ho, cattle, ho, ho, ho, ho!" Davy yelled. The cold water splashed onto his face. His horse stumbled, and Davy held on tightly. "Keep going," he said, "and don't fall."

His horse began to swim. It seemed like a long time before they reached the other side of the river. As the cattle came out of the icy water, they started running to get warm. A thousand longhorns pounded the dusty ground.

"Let them run!" Pa shouted. Old Blue would slow them down soon.

By late afternoon, the sky grew dark. Lightning flashed, and thunder boomed. There was another sound, too. Horns rattled together, and hooves pounded the dirt.

"Stampede!" Pa cried.

"Get out of the way, Davy!" he yelled. Davy rode his horse away from the frightened steers. He watched the cowboys guide Old Blue around in a circle. The cattle followed, and soon most of the herd were running in a big circle. That was called milling. It was the only way to stop a stampede.

"Whoa!" Davy cried, trying to calm his horse.

The air was full of electricity. Davy could see sparks dancing along the brim of his hat and on the tips of the horse's ears. Pa had called it foxfire. It even sparked from horn tip to horn tip over the milling cattle.

As soon as the herd had quieted down, Davy rode back to camp, where Cookie was at the chuck wagon building a fire.

"Get your slicker on," Cookie said. "It's going to be a bad night."

Davy put on his slicker and ate some cold biscuits and beans. "The wind is cold," he said.

Pa rode up to the chuck wagon. "We'll need every one of you in the saddle tonight," he said. "We can't let those longhorns stampede again."

"Do you want me to ride?" Davy asked.

Pa nodded. "I can use your help."

Davy pulled his hat lower over his eyes and rode out with the other cowboys.

Before midnight the rain turned to sleet. Davy could hear someone singing to keep the cattle calm. "Whoop-ee ti yi yo, git along little doggies!" If the longhorns stampeded in this storm, some could get lost and freeze before they were found.

It was the longest night Davy could ever remember. The sleet turned to snow, and Davy couldn't even see Old Blue.

By daylight, the worst of the storm was over. The cowboys took turns eating breakfast. Davy stood by the fire trying to get warm.

"You okay, Davy?" Pa asked.

"Just cold," Davy told him.

"Do you want to ride in the wagon with Cookie?" Pa asked him.

Davy shook his head. "No, sir."

"Good boy, Davy. Cookie, how do you ever keep a fire going in all this snow?"

"That's my secret," Cookie said.

"Hey, look who's here," Davy said. Old Blue came close for a bit of Davy's biscuit. "Old Blue, I almost lost you last night," he said, rubbing the steer between his horns. "When we get to Kansas City, I'm going to buy you a big bell to wear around your neck. Then I'll always know where you are," Davy said, "and so will the cattle."

"Nobody has ever belled a lead steer," Pa said, "but no steer was ever as tame as Old Blue. It's a good idea if it works."

"Davy, you don't have to wait until Kansas City," Cookie told him. "I've got a bell in the chuck wagon that you can use. I'll get it." He came back with a brass bell and a piece of rope.

Davy tied the bell around Old Blue's neck. "There you go, Old Blue. How do you like that?"

Old Blue shook his horns and listened to the bell clang.

"Just look how proud that old steer is," said Pa.

Davy gave Old Blue a hug. Old Blue shook his horns again and rang the bell louder than before. If a longhorn could smile, Old Blue would have.

305

Author

Sibyl Hancock's book *Old Blue* grew out of her Texas background. She says, "It's great fun to uncover interesting stories which have been almost overlooked by history and turn them into books for children." Old Blue was a real steer in early Texas days, and Mrs. Hancock has seen his horns preserved in a Texas museum.

Selection Wrap-up

Summary Questions

Old Blue helped Davy and the cowboys on the drive. Use these questions to tell how.

1. What problems did Davy and the cowboys have on the drive? How did Old Blue help them solve the problems?
2. Did Davy think Old Blue was special? What makes you think that?

3. Old Blue's horns are in an Old West museum in Texas. Tell why Davy might have remembered Old Blue and wanted the horns preserved.

The Reading and Writing Connection

Study the following chart. It gives some notes about one of Davy's days on the trail.

Time and Place	Day's Activities
Dawn in camp	Davy helped Cookie make breakfast.
Morning on trail	Davy rode at the front of the herd.
Afternoon on trail	There was almost a stampede!
Evening on trail	Davy rode with cowboys.

Pretend that you were on the trail with Davy. Use the notes to write a story called "A Day on the Trail with Old Blue." Try to use some words from the box.

steer	cattle	remarkable
sleet	plenty	saddle
stumbled	shivered	

Compound Words

Put the names of the pictures in each pair together to make a word.

When you put the names of each pair of pictures together, you made a word. Some words are made up of two shorter words.

A word that is made by putting two words together is called a **compound** word. *Flagpole, snowball, cornstalk,* and *mountaintop* are all compound words.

You can usually tell the meaning of a compound word if you know the meanings of the two short words.

A **flagpole** is a **pole** on which a **flag** can be displayed.

A **snowball** is a **ball** made out of **snow.**

A **cornstalk** is a **stalk** of **corn.**

A **mountaintop** is the **top** of a **mountain.**

308

Look at the four compound words below from the story "Old Blue." What two words have been put together to make each of these words?

campfire
tumbleweeds
longhorn
bedroll

On a separate piece of paper, copy the paragraph below. As you copy it, use compound words from the list above in place of the blanks.

Cowhands spend a lot of time outside. They drive a lot of _____ cattle over the plains. While they drive the cattle, they see hundreds of dry, bushy _____ blowing across the plains. At night the cowhands build a _____ to cook their dinner. Then they each get into a _____ to sleep under the stars.

Something Extra

Choose a partner. Each of you take several strips of paper and write one compound word on each strip. Then cut each strip of paper between the two words that are used to make the compound word.

Put the first part of each word in one container, and the second part of each word in another container.

Take turns choosing a word from each container. See if you and your partner can figure out the correct compound words. You might begin with words like *rattlesnake*, *pancake*, and *streetlight*.

Fact and Opinion

Often when you read, you see statements that are *facts* and statements that are *opinions.* Look at the pictures below and the statements below the pictures.

A
Tony has owned his dog Smoky for three years.

B
Tony thinks Smoky is the greatest dog in the world!

The statement under box A is a *fact.* A **fact** is something that can be checked to find out if it is true. You can find out whether Tony has owned his dog for three years by asking him or by asking his parents.

The statement under box B is an *opinion*. An **opinion** tells what a person thinks, feels, or believes. Tony *thinks* that his dog is the greatest in the world. Because Tony feels that way, that is his *opinion*. You may think your dog is the greatest dog in the world! Sometimes you will find words such as *think, feel, believe,* and *probably* in statements of opinion. These clue words will help you decide that a statement is an opinion.

Read these sentences and think about which one is a fact and which one is an opinion.

1. Susie hit two home runs in yesterday's game.
2. Maria thinks Susie is the best player on our team.

To decide whether a statement is a *fact,* ask this question: Can it be checked to prove whether it is true? If so, it is a fact.

Statement 1 is a fact. It tells you something that can be checked. Someone knows whether Susie hit two home runs in yesterday's game.

To decide whether a statement is an *opinion,* ask this question: Does the statement tell how someone feels or thinks? You can also ask: Does the statement contain any clue words, such as *think, feel, believe,* or *probably*? Statement 2 is an opinion. It tells you how Maria feels about Susie. The statement also contains the clue word *think.*

When you are reading or listening to information on television or on the radio, it is important to think about what you read or hear. Some things that are stated as facts are really only opinions. You need to decide whether something is a fact or an opinion.

Read this ad that Charlene saw in a magazine:

FISHING POLE

FOR SALE: The best fishing pole for a beginner. You'll catch the biggest fish. The pole weighs only 1 pound and is 5 feet long.

The first two sentences are opinions. They tell you what someone thinks about this fishing pole. The last sentence is a fact. It tells you something that can be checked.

Recognizing Fact and Opinion

Read each of the statements below. Decide whether it is a *fact* or an *opinion*. Remember to ask yourself the questions that can help you decide.

1. Richard thinks that playing basketball is better exercise than biking.
2. A baseball is smaller than a basketball.
3. Trent School is the largest school in our town.
4. Anna believes the students in our school are friendlier than the students at Main School.
5. Cats are better pets than dogs.
6. Turtles, snakes, and crocodiles are all reptiles.

Skill Summary

- A fact is something that can be checked to prove whether it is true.
- An opinion tells what a person thinks, feels, or believes. Sometimes clue words such as *think, feel, believe,* and *probably* can help you decide that a statement is an opinion.
- Some things you read or hear appear to be facts, but they are really opinions. Deciding whether something is a fact or an opinion will help you become a better reader and listener.

The Rooster Who Understood Japanese

by Yoshiko Uchida

Mrs. K. was leading a happy life with her pets and visits from her special friend Miyo. But one day something happens to change all that. Will Miyo be able to help?

"Mrs. K.!" Miyo called. "I'm here!"

Every afternoon when Miyo came home from school, she went to the home of her neighbor, Mrs. Kitamura, whom she called "Mrs. K."

This was because Miyo's mother was a doctor at University Hospital and didn't get home until suppertime.

It was a fine arrangement all around. Mrs. K.'s husband had died, and she enjoyed Miyo's company. Not that she was lonely. She had a basset hound named Jefferson, a parrot named Hamilton, a black cat named Leonardo, and a pet rooster named Mr. Lincoln. She talked to all of them in Japanese.

About the time Miyo came home from school, Mrs. K. was usually outside, talking to her animals, but today Mrs. K. was nowhere to be seen.

Miyo stopped to see Mr. Lincoln. He was strutting about in his pen making rooster-like sounds and looking very intelligent and dignified. Mrs. K. had told Miyo that he understood every word she said to him, in English or Japanese.

"Mrs. Kitamura, *doko?*" Miyo said, asking Mr. Lincoln where Mrs. K. was. He cocked his head, looked at her with his small bright eyes, and uttered a squawking sound.

Miyo shrugged her shoulders. Maybe Mr. Lincoln did understand Japanese, but it didn't do her any good if she couldn't understand what he said back.

"Never mind," she said. "I'll find her." And she hurried toward the house. The back door was unlatched, and Miyo walked in.

"Mrs. K., I'm here," she called once more.

Immediately a high shrill voice repeated, "Mrs. K., I'm here." It was Hamilton, the parrot.

"Hello, Hamilton," Miyo said.

"Hello, Hamilton," he answered back.

Miyo went into the dining room and found Mrs. K. sitting at the big dining room table. She was doing something Miyo had never seen her do before. She was making herself a cup of ceremonial Japanese tea. She was stirring the special green tea in a beautiful tea bowl.

Mrs. K. looked startled. "I was so busy with my thoughts, I didn't even hear you come in."

Miyo looked at the pale green tea, knowing it was strong and bitter. "Is that our afternoon tea?" she asked, trying not to look too disappointed.

"No, no, not yours," Mrs. K. answered quickly. "Just mine. I made it to calm myself." She turned the bowl around carefully and drank it in the proper three and a half sips. "There," she sighed.

"Are you calm now?" Miyo asked.

Mrs. K. shook her head. "Not really. Actually, not at all. As a matter of fact, I am most upset."

Miyo wondered why Mrs. K. was so upset. Usually she was full of fun, but today she scarcely smiled at Miyo.

"I've been upset since seven o'clock this morning," she explained suddenly.

"Why?" Miyo asked. "Did you get out of the wrong side of the bed?"

That was what her mother sometimes asked when Miyo was grumpy, but that wasn't Mrs. K.'s trouble at all.

"It's not me," she said. "It's my new neighbor, Mr. Wickett. He told me that if Mr. Lincoln didn't stop waking him up by crowing at six in the morning, he was going to report me to the police for disturbing the peace! Can you imagine anything so unfriendly?"

"That's mean," Miyo said.

"What am I going to do?" Mrs. K. asked. "I can't go out and tell Mr. Lincoln he is not to crow anymore. That would be like telling Jefferson not to wag his tail, or telling Leonardo not to groom himself. . . ."

"Or telling Hamilton not to imitate us," Miyo said.

"Exactly," Mrs. K. agreed. "He is only behaving in his natural rooster-like way."

Miyo wondered what she could say to make Mrs. K. feel better, and finally she said, "I'll ask my mother. She'll know what to do."

Miyo's mother usually found a way to solve most problems.

"Don't worry, Mama will think of something," Miyo said as she left Mrs. Kitamura's house.

Mrs. K. nodded. "I hope so," she said sadly. "In the meantime, I must think of something before six o'clock tomorrow morning."

When Miyo got home, Mother called, "Hi Miyo, how was Mrs. K. today?"

"She was worried," Miyo answered as she began to set the table. "She's got to make Mr. Lincoln stop crowing."

"Whatever for?"

Miyo quickly told Mother about Mr. Wickett. "Isn't that mean?" she said. "Mr. Lincoln doesn't hurt anybody."

"Well, I can see Mr. Wickett's side too," Mother said. "Mr. Lincoln doesn't bother us because we're up anyway. If I could sleep late, I'm not so sure I'd like having a rooster wake me at six o'clock. Besides," she added, "our town is growing, and we're in the city limits now. Maybe Mrs. K. will just have to give Mr. Lincoln away."

Miyo didn't even want to think of such a thing. "Mr. Lincoln's not just any old rooster," she said.

"I know," Mother agreed. "Maybe we can think of something."

But nobody could. Not Mother, not Miyo, and not Mrs. K.

That first night Mrs. K. brought Mr. Lincoln inside the house and put him into a big cardboard carton in her bedroom.

"Poor Mr. Lincoln," she said to Miyo the next day. "He nearly smothered, and I hardly got any sleep at all. He crowed in the morning anyway, but I don't think Mr. Wickett heard him because so far the police haven't come. Still I jump every time my doorbell rings. What on earth are we going to do?"

Miyo wished she had an answer, yet all she could say was, "Mama and I are both thinking hard."

Mother just couldn't think of any good ideas. She did say, however, that keeping Mr. Lincoln inside a carton in the house was not the answer.

And Mrs. K. certainly found out it wasn't. On the second night she brought him inside, Mr. Lincoln pecked his way right out of the carton and walked all over the house. He scratched the floors and pecked at her sofa and got into a fight with Leonardo, the cat. By the time Mrs. K. got to them, there were feathers all over her living room.

"I suppose I will have to give Mr. Lincoln away," Mrs. K. murmured sadly. "But I can't give him to just anybody. It has to be someone who will love him and not turn him into fricassee or stew."

Miyo thought and thought. Then, suddenly, she had an idea.

"I know," she said brightly. "I'll put an ad in our class newspaper."

Miyo's class newspaper was almost ready for the month of October. There were several sections, one each for news, feature stories, science, book reviews, sports, poems, and, finally, a small section for ads. That's where Miyo thought Mr. Lincoln would fit nicely.

Miyo made her ad very special. She wrote, "Wanted: Nice home for friendly, intelligent, dignified rooster. P.S. He understands Japanese." Then she added, "Please hurry! Urgent!"

Miyo's teacher, Mrs. Fielding, told her it was a fine ad. She suggested that Miyo include her phone number, so Miyo did. Miyo also drew a picture of Mr. Lincoln beneath her ad, trying to make him look dignified and friendly.

The very day the newspaper came out a police officer rang the doorbell at Mrs. K.'s house.

"I've a complaint, Ma'm," he said, "about a rooster?" He seemed to think there might have been some mistake.

Mrs. K. sighed. "Come inside, officer," she said. "I've been expecting you."

"I'm sorry," the officer said, "but I have to tell you that you're breaking a city law by having a rooster in your yard."

"Even if I'm only barely inside the city limits?" Mrs. K. asked.

The officer nodded. "I'm afraid so. I'll give you two more days to get rid of your rooster. Mr. Wickett says you're disturbing the peace."

While the police officer was at Mrs. K.'s house, Miyo was at school reading the class newspaper. She was thinking how proud she was of her ad, but no one seemed at all interested in Mr. Lincoln. Instead, several people told her how much they liked her news story about Mr. Botts, the school custodian, who was retiring.

She had written, "Say good-by to the best custodian Hawthorn School ever had. After working hard here for many years, Mr. Botts is retiring. He and Mrs. Botts are moving to Far Creek. He is going to eat a lot and sleep a lot and maybe go fishing. So, so long, Mr. Botts. And good luck!"

On her way home, Miyo ran into Mr. Botts himself. He told her it was the first time in his entire life that anyone had written a news story about him.

When he got home that night, he read the class newspaper from cover to cover. At the top of one page, he saw Miyo's ad about Mr. Lincoln.

"Tami," he said to Mrs. Botts, who happened to be Japanese, "how would you like to have a rooster that understands Japanese?"

"A what?"

"A rooster that understands Japanese," Mr. Botts repeated. "When we move, didn't you say you were going to grow vegetables and raise chickens while I go fishing?"

Mrs. Botts remembered having said something like that. "Yes, I guess I did."

"Well, how would you like a rooster, too?"

"Why, I guess I would."

"Then we might as well have one that's friendly and dignified," Mr. Botts said, and he went right to the telephone to call Miyo.

"I'll take that rooster you want to find a home for," he said. "My wife, Tami, could talk to it in Japanese, too."

Miyo couldn't believe it. Someone had actually read her ad and that somebody was Mr. Botts. Mr. and Mrs. Botts would give Mr. Lincoln a fine home and surely wouldn't turn him into fricassee or stew. At last, she had done something to help Mrs. K. As soon as she told Mother, she ran right over to tell Mrs. K. the good news.

"Hooray! *Banzai!*" Mrs. K. said happily. "Tomorrow night we will have a party to celebrate. I shall invite you and your mama, and Mr. and Mrs. Botts." And because Mrs. K. felt so relieved and happy, she even decided to invite Mr. Wickett.

"Even though you are a cross old man," she said to Mr. Wickett, "I suppose you were right. A rooster shouldn't live in a small pen at the edge of town. He should live in the country where he'll have some hens to talk to and nobody will care if he crows at the sun."

Mr. Wickett was a little embarrassed to come to Mrs. K.'s party, but he was too lonely to say no. He came with some flowers and said, "I'm sorry I caused such a fuss."

Mrs. K. told him he needn't be sorry. "Life needs a little stirring up now and then," she said. "Besides," she added, "now both Mr. Lincoln and I have found new friends."

After the party, Mr. Botts carried Mr. Lincoln in his crate to his station wagon. Mr. Lincoln gave a polite squawk of farewell and Mrs. K. promised she would come visit him soon.

"Good-by, Mr. Lincoln. Good-by, Mr. and Mrs. Botts," Miyo called.

From inside Mrs. K.'s kitchen, Hamilton, the parrot, screeched. "Good-by, Mr. Lincoln. Good-by."

Then Mr. Botts honked his horn and drove off.

"I hope we'll see each other again soon," Mr. Wickett said to Mrs. K.

"Good night, Mr. Wickett," she answered. "I'm sure we will."

Miyo and her mother thanked Mrs. K. for the nice party and went home.

"Do you think Mrs. K. will miss Mr. Lincoln a lot?" Miyo asked.

"She will for a while," Mother answered, "but now she has a new friend and neighbor to talk to."

Miyo nodded. That was true. She was glad everything had turned out so well, and she went to bed feeling very good inside.

Author

"Although I was born in California," says Yoshiko Uchida, "a good bit of Japan was inside me all along, for this was the country from which my parents came." Besides folk tales for older readers, Miss Uchida's outstanding books include many about real life. All her books are about Japanese or Japanese-American children.

Selection Wrap-up

Summary Questions

Mr. Lincoln was a good pet but a bad neighbor. Use these questions to tell why.

1. Why was Mr. Lincoln a good pet for Mrs. K.? Why was he a bad neighbor for Mr. Wickett?
2. What was Mrs. K.'s problem? How did Miyo help Mrs. K. solve her problem?
3. Help Miyo write a feature story about Mr. Lincoln and how he got a new home. Make up a headline. Then tell what Miyo might write.

The Reading and Writing Connection

Choose one of Mrs. K.'s pets, pictured above. Pretend that it needs a new home. Write an ad to find a new home for the pet. Be sure to tell about the pet, what it looks like, and why it needs a home. Try to use some words from the box.

arrangement	intelligent	dignified
scarcely	limits	urgent
immediately	farewell	

The HAWTHORN SCHOOL NEWS

Mr. Botts Retires

Say good—by to the best custodian Hawthorn School ever had. After working hard here for many years, Mr. Botts is retiring. He and Mrs. Botts are moving to Far Creek. He is going to eat a lot and sleep a lot and maybe go fishing. So, so long, Mr. Botts. And good luck!

HAWTHORN SCHOOL WINS

Hawthorn School's best runners raced with runners from Park Street School. Hawthorn School won every race!

Jeff Marks won two races and Jane Wong won three races.

It was the most exciting event of the school year.

"CHUCKLES"

Where does February come before January?

in a dictionary

Jim: What's the name of your dog?
Kim: Ginger.
Jim: Does Ginger bite?
Kim: No, Ginger snaps!

GATSBY the GREAT COMES TO HAWTHORN

Gatsby the Great came to our school last month. She performed many tricks.

Everyone's favorite trick was the Disappearing Homework Trick. Gatsby copied down some words on a paper. When she showed it to us, the words had disappeared! Then she held the paper near a light and -- presto-- the words appeared!

Before she left, Gatsby told us her secret. She wrote the words with milk!

• WANTED •

Nice home for friendly, intelligent, dignified rooster. P.S. He understands Japanese. Please hurry! Urgent! Call Miyo.

☞ for sale

One-year-old bike. 10 speed. Greatest bike in town. Could use some paint.

Reading in Social Studies: Textbook

Producing a Newspaper

Modern day printing press

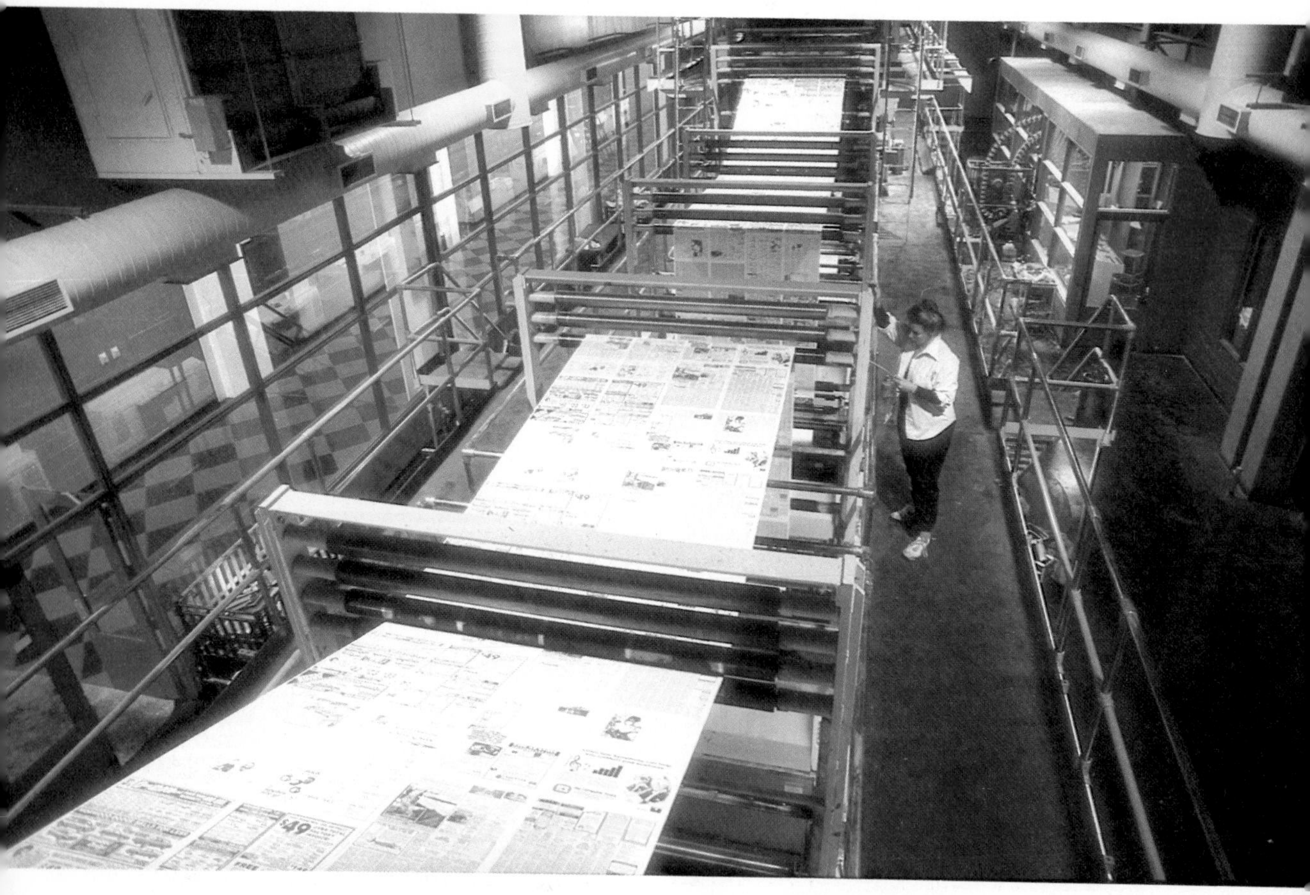

Newspapers are an important source of information in a community. You can find out what is happening in your city, in your country, and in the world by reading a newspaper. A newspaper has news, stories, ads, and other useful information.

It takes many different people doing many different jobs to get the news to you.

Editor discussing assignment with reporter

Getting the News

In most big cities, newspapers are printed at least once a day. Because they come out so often, the news must be fresh. **Reporters** are the people who gather the news. They interview people to get information for their stories. Sometimes they have to look up the information to be sure that what they report is true.

Reporter interviewing sailors from historic ship

Above: Getting information off of wire service

Left: Reporter interviewing marathon runner

Some reporters work in only one area, called a **beat.** The beat may be a place, such as a police department. Or it may be a subject, such as sports. News from other cities and other parts of the world often comes from **wire services.** These services have reporters all around the world. They send their stories and pictures through special machines to newspapers. The newspaper then pays the wire service.

Writing the News

Reporters start their stories with the most important facts. These are answers to the *who, what, where,* and *when* questions. These facts are often put in the first paragraph of a story, which is called the **lead.** The rest of the story gives more information about the lead, and may include answers to the *why* and *how* questions.

Reporters type their stories on what looks like a typewriter. However, they may not see what they have written on paper. They see it on a **video display terminal,** or **VDT.**

Reporter working at video display terminal, reviewing story

Editing the News

The story then goes to the **assigning editor.** The assigning editor checks to see that the story has enough information.

The editors and the **managing editor** decide where in the newspaper the story should be placed.

Then a **copy editor** gets the story. The copy editor checks to be sure the story is well written and fits the space. The copy editor also writes a **headline** for the story. The headline is the large print at the top of a news story. It tells you what the story is about.

Editors working together on layouts

Other Parts of a Newspaper

Not everything you see in a newspaper is a news story. Some stories are **features,** and some are **editorials.**

Features are stories that have facts, but they are written more to capture your interest than to inform you of facts. Features may be written on any subject the editor thinks will interest readers. Travel, famous people, and fashion are often the subjects of features.

Editorials are written to give **opinions.** An opinion is the way a person thinks or feels about something.

The people who run a newspaper often write editorials. They find an important **issue,** or topic. They tell you how they feel about it or what they think should be done about it. The people who write editorials include facts to back up their opinions. But they also use words that try to persuade people to think the way they do.

Photographer on assignment at community event

Reporters writing stories on VDT in busy newspaper office

338

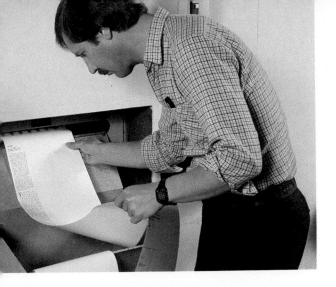

Production worker removing galleys from typesetter

Taking trimmed galleys and positioning them on make-up pages

Ads, movie reviews, puzzles, and comics help make up the rest of most newspapers.

Printing the Newspapers

The photograph on page 334 shows a large printing plant where type is set and pages are put together. It also shows the huge press on which the newspaper is printed.

Another machine cuts and folds the pages. The folded papers are taken on a moving belt to a mail room where they are put into bundles.

Folded papers being taken off belt of same printing press as seen on page 334

Delivering the Newspapers

Bundled newspapers are loaded onto delivery trucks. These trucks take the newspapers to different places.

Some newspapers are taken to newsstands where people can buy them. Other newspapers are taken to paper carriers. They deliver the papers to homes on their routes. Still other newspapers are taken to the post office and are delivered with the mail. How do you get your newspaper?

No matter how you get your newspaper, you can get a lot of information from it.

Trucks being loaded in preparation for distribution of newspapers

Newspaper carriers preparing newspapers for delivery

Summary Questions

1. Tell about some of the things reporters do.
2. What are some of the questions reporters try to answer in their stories?
3. Explain how reporters use a video display terminal.
4. Not everything you see in a newspaper is a news story. What are some other types of stories? Tell about them.
5. What happens to the newspaper after it is printed?
6. How do the newspapers get to the people who want to read them?

Reporting Activity

Pretend that you are a reporter. Write an article about something interesting that has happened in your town or in your classroom lately. Remember to answer the questions *who*, *what*, *where*, *when*, *why*, and *how*.

Subject Area Words

Many jobs have their own special words that describe things having to do with that type of work. These words are understood by other people who do the same kind of work.

People who help produce newspapers use special words. Here are just a few of them and their meanings.

beat   An area or subject a reporter usually reports on.

city room   Community news department.

cut   To take out copy to fit a space.

deadline   A set time by which something must be finished.

edit   To correct, check, or change writing.

editorial   A story written to tell how a person thinks or feels about something.

feature   A story with facts written on any subject of interest to readers.

interview   A conversation to get information.

reporter   A person who gathers and reports news.

Reading newspapers is one way to get information. Read the following to find out what people in a newspaper office do in order to get information into a newspaper. Use the part of a glossary on page 342 to find the meanings of words you don't know.

People in the **city room** work hard to finish stories before the **deadline**.

One writer **edits** a **feature** story about a new place to visit. Another prepares an **editorial** about an important issue.

As stories come in on the wire services, an editor reads them and decides what copy should be **cut**.

At one of many video display terminals, a **reporter** types the most important parts of her **interview** with someone.

Suddenly, a news reporter comes in with some last minute information he has gathered while on his **beat**.

The city room of a newspaper is certainly a very busy place!

Copy the sentences below onto a piece of paper. Then use some of the words from the glossary on page 342 in place of the blanks.

1. Dan came running into the _____.
2. The _____ was only minutes away.
3. Dan still had to _____ his story to correct any mistakes.
4. He had written a _____ story that gave information about a new hobby.
5. Another _____ had helped Dan gather the information.
6. Most of the information came from an _____ with someone.

Magazine Wrap-up

Story Settings

Think about the stories "Benny's Flag," "The Skates of Uncle Richard," "Old Blue," and "The Rooster Who Understood Japanese." Which of the stories took place long ago? Which of the stories could happen today? *Where* did these stories take place? Tell why you answered each question as you did.

Vocabulary

Look at the words below. Can you name a category for each column of words? Tell why you chose that category.

tern	oysters
gull	mussels
parrot	barnacles
Canada goose	minnows

Now look at the names of these two categories:

Containers
Action Words

Which words below belong in the category **Action Words?** Which words belong in the category **Containers?** Are there words that could be in both categories?

strut	box
crate	wander
scurry	sack
bag	crawl
stumble	carton
skating	plunge

Fact or Opinion

You have learned that some statements are *facts* and some are *opinions*. A *fact* is something that can be checked to find out if it is true. An *opinion* tells what a person thinks, feels, or believes.

Copy each sentence. Beside it write *fact* if it gives a fact. Write *opinion* if it gives an opinion.

1. Juneau is the capital of Alaska.
2. I think my new ice skates are the best in the world.
3. Tom is the youngest boy in our class.
4. Ann believes this newspaper is the most interesting newspaper in our city.
5. Your basset hound is the friendliest dog in our state.

Books to Enjoy

The Biggest Living Thing
by Caroline Arnold

The biggest living things in the world are the giant sequoias, the huge trees in California.

Stories Julian Tells
by Ann Cameron

Here are six short stories about a young boy and his family and his new friend.

Grandmama's Joy
by Eloise Greenfield

A little girl tries to make her grandmother feel happy when the family has to move.

Ming Lo Moves the Mountain by Arnold Lobel

In this funny story, a man in China finds a way to get away from living close to the mountain.

The Two Stonecutters

**written by
Eve Titus**

**illustrated by
Haru Wells**

Long ago in a small village, there lived two brothers who were stonecutters. While working in the forest one day, the brothers quite unexpectedly were granted seven wishes to share. Younger Brother and Elder Brother had very different ideas about what to do with their wishes. These wishes changed the life of one of the brothers more than he could ever have imagined.

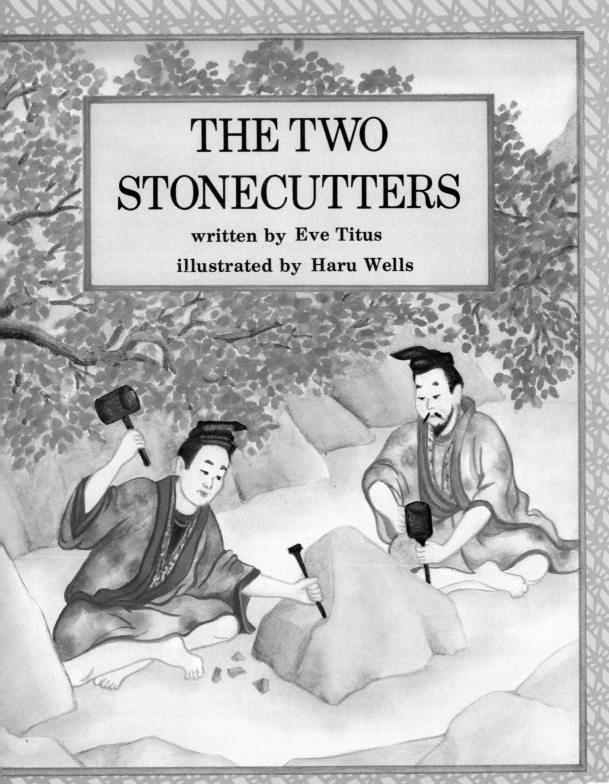

THE TWO STONECUTTERS

written by Eve Titus

illustrated by Haru Wells

Long ago in a faraway land there lived two brothers who were stonecutters. Side by side stood their little huts, on the edge of a forest. And side by side the brothers entered the forest each day, seeking stones to use as building blocks. Finding such a stone, they would chip patiently away with their tools until it was of the right shape and size.

Younger Brother was content to be a humble stonecutter, as their father had been, and their father's father before him. Happily he listened to the songs of the birds, and admired the blue of the sky, and watched the forest animals at play.

Elder Brother did none of these things. He was not content to be a humble stonecutter, but longed to be rich and mighty and powerful.

One morning, on their way through the forest, the brothers met an old, old woman with a cane. "Good Stonecutters," said she, "I am *so* weary — will you let me lean upon your shoulders?"

So swiftly did they move that she could not tell which one offered his shoulder first.

Then she said, "Good Stonecutters, I am *so* thirsty — will you let me have a small sip of water?"

So swiftly did they move that she could not tell which one offered his cup first.

Then she said, "Good Stonecutters, I am *so* hungry — will you let me have a little food?"

So swiftly did they move that she could not tell which one offered his food first.

Suddenly they saw a flash of golden light! A radiantly beautiful being stood before them — the Queen of the Forest! Covering their eyes, they fell to the ground.

"Rise, Good Kind Stonecutters!" she commanded. "I pretended to be an old woman to test you. I shall reward your kindness with seven wishes — divide them as you choose."

The brothers bowed low, and spoke their thanks.

Then Younger Brother thought for a while, and said "But I *need* no wishes, for I am a happy man. Elder Brother may have all seven!"

The Queen frowned. "Younger Brother, you must keep one wish. It may happen that one day you may find a use for it."

"Very well," he replied. "Six for my brother, and one for myself."

"So be it!" said the Queen of the Forest, and vanished.

Elder Brother said to Younger Brother, "It was good of you to give me those extra wishes. Now I shall be rich and mighty and powerful, the happiest man in the world."

Younger Brother smiled sadly. "How I shall miss you! Good luck, wherever your wishes may take you."

Elder Brother embraced him fondly, and said, "I shall always think lovingly of you, Dear Brother. Still, these wishes must not be wasted. Farewell!"

Quickly he wished the first wish, saying, "From Stonecutter to — Rich Man! I wish to be a Rich Man."

And faster than a deer running —
he was a Rich Man!!!

He sat in a fine house, with fine furnishings, and many servants to do his bidding.

That afternoon Elder Brother went riding in a splendid carriage attended by brave warriors clad in shining armor.

And he was content, and said, "How mighty am I! Now I shall always be happy."

But along came the magnificent carriage of a Prince, attended not only by warriors in shining armor, but also by nobles clad in cloth of gold. People on the road bowed low before the prince. Elder Brother had to wait at the side of the road until the Prince's carriage had passed.

This will never do, thought Elder Brother — a Prince is mightier than a Rich Man.

By morning his mind was made up. Eagerly he wished the second wish, saying, "From Stonecutter to Rich Man to — Prince! I wish to be a Prince."

And faster than a star falling —
he was a Prince!!!

He dwelt in a palace of more than a hundred rooms, each more beautiful than the next. Wearing robes of richest velvet, he roamed through the palace gardens, where peacocks paraded for his pleasure.

That afternoon Elder Brother rode in a magnificent carriage, attended by brave warriors and many great nobles. People bowed their heads respectfully, and other carriages halted until he had passed.

And he was content, and said, "How mighty am I! Now I shall always be happy."

But suddenly the Wind came, whistling and wailing! The Wind blew with such force that all had to halt, powerless to move a single step. The Wind made the leaves leap from the trees, and sent streams rushing into rivers.

The Wind snatched the hat from Elder Brother's head, blowing it high into the air and out of sight!

This will never do, thought Elder Brother — the Wind is mightier than a Prince.

By morning his mind was made up. Calmly he wished the third wish, saying, "From Stone-cutter to Rich Man to Prince to — Wind! I wish to be the Wind!"

And faster than a top spinning —
he was the Wind!!!

What a time he had, huffing and puffing all over the world! He whipped the waves of the seven seas higher and higher and higher, tossing ships about like toy sailboats.

On land he lifted up the dust, and whirled it around and around. People hid indoors, afraid to be blown away. Even trees thousands of years old bent and swayed before his great strength.

And he was content, and said, "How mighty am I! Now I shall always be happy."

Then the Sun came, with its burning rays.

The heat was heavy upon the land, and people slowed their steps and had to take shelter in the cooling shade. Beneath the burning rays of the Sun, the Wind grew weak and was soon no more than a gentle breeze.

This will never do, thought Elder Brother — the Sun is mightier than the Wind.

Almost at once he made up his mind. Slowly he wished the fourth wish, saying, "From Stonecutter to Rich Man to Prince to Wind to — Sun! I wish to be the Sun."

And faster than a bird flying —
he was the Sun!!!

What a time he had, beaming upon the far corners of the world! He dried up hills and dales, and lakes and streams. He made the flowers hang their heads, and wilt, and die.

High in the heavens he climbed, burning bright, blazing bright. And he was content, and said, "How mighty am I! Now I shall always be happy."

But suddenly a Stormcloud came, outspread across the sky! Down poured the rain on the highways and byways. People sat huddled in their huts, fearful of the falling hailstones. Lightning flashed, thunder crashed, and all was dark, for the Stormcloud had blotted out the Sun!

This will never do, thought Elder Brother — the Stormcloud is mightier than the Sun.

Only two wishes remain, he told himself — but I must, I shall, I *will* be happy! Sadly he wished the fifth wish. "From Stonecutter to Rich Man to Prince to Wind to Sun to — Stormcloud! I wish to be the Stormcloud."

And faster than a ball rolling —
he was the Stormcloud!!!

What a time he had, raging and roaring all over the world! He sent forth a terrible downpour that made muddy brown streams of the roads. Rivers went tumbling into towns and washed away houses and bridges, and people fled before the flood. Bowing down to the heavy rains, the high grass lay flat along the ground. It seemed that nothing in the world could withstand the wildness of the storm!

And he was content, and said, "How mighty am I! Now I shall always be happy!"

Then he noticed that no matter how he tried, he could not move a certain stone in the forest. The Stone was huge and would not budge an inch, nor bend nor bow before him. And though he sent down torrents of rain, the Stone would not be washed away — all his power was as nothing!

This will never do, thought Elder Brother — the Stone is mightier than the Stormcloud.

Only one wish is left, he thought. "Will the last be the best?"

Sadly he wished the sixth wish, saying, "From Stonecutter to Rich Man to Prince to Wind to Sun to Stormcloud to — Stone! I wish to be the Stone."

And faster than a fish swimming —
he was the Stone!!!

He rested firmly on the floor of the forest, and not Storm nor Sun nor Wind could move him. The forest was fragrant, and mossy, and cool. In the mornings he was awakened by the chatter of little monkeys, and at night the birds sang him to sleep.

The forest was pleasant and peaceful. Days and then weeks went by, like a dream. At last Elder Brother was *truly* content, and said, "How mighty am I! Now I shall always be happy!"

But one morning the monkeys were strangely silent, and he heard a sound that filled him with fear —

the sound of stonecutters at work!!!

"How mighty I am *not!*" said he, "for now I am at the mercy of any stonecutter who happens by."

He had not long to wait. A hand patted him, and a voice said, "Great Stone, I want you for the Emperor's new palace."

Elder Brother recognized the voice, and cried out, "Younger Brother, Younger Brother! It is I! Spare me, I beg of you, for we are brothers! I am the Stone you spoke to — do you not know me?" But he was too terrified to talk clearly.

Younger Brother looked all around him. "I heard a voice, whose words I did not understand. Yet there is no one here but myself!"

Greatly puzzled, he went back to the Stone, saying, "I must have imagined the voice, for I see no one." And he took out his tools, ready to go to work.

Elder Brother cried out a second time. "Younger Brother, Younger Brother! It is I! I beg you, I beseech you to put down your tools! I am the Stone, but I am also your brother — how can you stand there and not know me?" But fear weakened his voice even more than before, and again his words were not clear.

Younger Brother dropped his tools in surprise. "Did I hear a voice, or are my ears playing tricks?" He climbed to the top of the tallest tree, and looked everywhere, but saw no one, no one at all. Still puzzled, he returned to the Stone, and picked up the tools, ready to go to work.

Elder Brother wept, and cried out a third time. This time the Queen of the Forest, who had been listening, took pity on Elder Brother, and his words rang loud and clear! "Younger Brother, Younger Brother! It is I! It is Elder Brother who begs you, who beseeches you, who entreats you to put away your tools! Do you not hear my words? I am the Stone!"

And at last Younger Brother heard the words, and wept. He leaned against the Stone, saying, "O, my poor brother! How did you come to this?"

Elder Brother told him everything, and then said, "You must build a high fence around me, to save me from other stonecutters. Younger Brother, will you visit me sometimes?"

Younger Brother smiled, "I will do even more! I forgot all about my own wish, for I am a happy man. What better time to use it than here and now?"

Lovingly Younger Brother wished his one wish. "From Stonecutter to Rich Man to Prince to Wind to Sun to Stormcloud to Stone to — Stonecutter! I wish my brother to be what he was."

And faster than a page turning —
Elder Brother was himself!!!

Gladly the brothers embraced, together at last.

From that day on Elder Brother was content, and the two stonecutters lived happily, side by side in their little huts on the edge of the forest.

Summary Questions

1. What happened when the two brothers unexpectedly met the Queen of the Forest?
2. What did Younger Brother do with his wishes? What did Elder Brother wish for?
3. Which brother do you think was the wiser of the two? What makes you think that?

Author

Eve Titus is the author of a number of children's books set in foreign countries. *The Two Stonecutters*, an old folktale that she adapted from the Japanese, takes place in Japan. Her popular and funny *Anatole* books are about a cheese-tasting mouse in Paris, France. Two books in this series were named Caldecott Honor Books. Her *Basil* series tells about a detective mouse in London, England. Some of the Basil adventures also take place in Mexico, Switzerland, and Asia. Well traveled herself, Ms. Titus has also been a concert pianist and a lecturer.

Illustrator

Haru Wells grew up in Buenos Aires, Argentina, in South America. There she learned to do oriental silk painting as a child and later went to art school. Ms. Wells has illustrated many children's books, among them a Japanese historical novel for older children, which won a National Book Award for Children's Literature. Her artwork also includes oil painting, sculpture, puppetry, and animated TV cartoons.

Glossary

This glossary can help you find out the meanings of many of the words in this book. The meanings given are the meanings of the words as the words are used in the book. Sometimes a second meaning is also given.

A

accounts Written records of money spent or received.

actually In fact, really.

advice A suggestion about what to do.

affect To bring about a change in: *The weather affects my moods.*

alarm **1.** Sudden fear caused by a feeling of danger. **2.** A bell or buzzer to warn people or to wake them up.

amusement park A park with rides, games, and food stands.

anchor To hold in place: *Let's anchor our boat in the harbor.*

ankle The joint where the foot meets the leg.

anxious Eager: *We were anxious to get to the park and have a picnic.*

appetite The desire for food: *After the hike the children had a big appetite.*

appreciate To understand the worth or importance of something; to value highly.

arrangement An agreement or plan for doing something.

assign To give out a task or job.

assistant Someone who helps.

attach To fasten on or connect: *I attached a pin to my jacket.*

attack To make a sudden move against.

attend To wait on: *Many servants attended the king.*

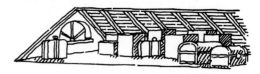

attic A space in a house just under the roof: *An attic may be used for storage.*

aunt The sister of a person's father or mother.

autumn The season of the year between summer and winter; the fall.

awful Very bad or unpleasant.

awkwardly In a clumsy way: *I moved awkwardly in the duck costume.*

B

banquet A large meal, usually to celebrate something special.

barnacle A small, hard-shelled sea animal that attaches itself to rocks and to the bottoms of ships.

bass A North American fish used for food.

basset hound A dog with a long, heavily built body, short legs, and long, drooping ears.

beak The hard, pointed mouth parts of a bird; a bill.

beaver An animal with thick fur, a broad, flat tail, and large, strong front teeth.

bend **1.** To move part of the body lower; bow: *Can you bend to pick up the ball?* **2.** To take or cause to take a new direction: *The road bends to the left at the store.*

beseech To ask in a serious way; beg: *I beseech you to set me free.*

blind Unable to see through the eyes.

blossom A flower: *The apple trees have lovely blossoms on them.*

blunt Having an edge or point that is not sharp: *The knife is too blunt to cut the meat.*

blur Something that is hard to see or not clear: *The spinning top was a blur.*

blurt To say something without thinking: *The student blurted out the answer without being called on.*

brag To speak highly about oneself: *Nobody likes to listen to a person who brags too much.*

briefly In a few words or for a short amount of time.

brush 1. A tool for scrubbing, making something neat, or putting on liquids: *A brush has bristles and a handle.* 2. To wipe lightly or touch: *The dog brushed my leg as it ran by.*

burro A small donkey, usually used for riding or for carrying things.

burrow 1. A hole, tunnel, or opening dug in the ground by a small animal: *The rabbits hid in the burrows.* 2. To dig into: *The woodchuck will burrow into its hole.*

C

calf The young of certain large animals, such as cattle or moose.

calves A form of the word *calf.* Several of the young of certain large animals.

capital A city where the government of a state or country is located: *Augusta is the capital of Maine.*

carriage Something to ride in, often with four wheels and pulled by horses.

cattle Animals that have horns and are raised for meat and milk; cows, bulls, and oxen.

cello A musical instrument of the violin family.

champion Someone or something known for being the best.

clad A form of the word *clothe.* Dressed: *We clad ourselves in bright costumes.*

clever Showing skill or quick thinking: *The scouts had a clever plan.*

clock Something that tells the time.

collect To get payment of: *He wanted to collect the money the woman owed him.*

company 1. Companionship: *She was glad to have her mother's company on the long plane trip.* 2. A business: *Many people work for this company.*

compartment A separate section: *My desk has a compartment for pencils.*

complain To say that one is unhappy or annoyed.

contain To have within itself; hold: *The carton contained books and toys.*

370

continent One of the main land masses of the earth. The seven continents are Africa, Asia, Antarctica, Australia, Europe, North America, and South America.

continue To go on; begin again after stopping: *Our program will continue after a short break.*

conversation Talk between two or more people.

cornstalk A stem of the corn plant.

court A place where or an event when a judge hears cases: *The king held court to decide how to defend the land.*

coyote An animal that looks like a wolf.

creak To make a squeaky sound.

creep To move slowly; crawl.

crept A form of the word *creep.* Moved slowly.

current 1. Water that is moving: *The current moved the boat.* 2. Of the present time: *This is my current address.*

curtain A piece of cloth or other material hung at a window to shut out the light.

custodian A person who takes care of a building: *The custodian went to get the broom.*

D

dawn The first light that shows in the morning; the time when the first light appears.

debt Something that is owed: *We paid our debt to the bank.*

delicious Very pleasing to the taste or smell.

delight Great pleasure, joy: *After answering the question, I smiled in delight.*

den The home of a wild animal.

design 1. A pattern of lines, figures, or objects. 2. To prepare a plan for something, especially by drawing.

determine 1. To decide or settle something: *I was determined to do well.* 2. To find out: *The winner was determined by counting the votes.*

diary A record written each day of a person's own experiences.

dignified Important; respectable; serious: *A dignified crowd attended the concert.*

discourage   To take away hope: *I was discouraged about my chances of making the team.*

discovery   Something found for the first time: *The discovery of dinosaur bones is exciting.*

disguise   **1.** Something that changes or hides a person's appearance. **2.** To change or hide one's identity.

disturb   To upset; bother: *The party is so loud that it is disturbing the peace.*

double   Two times as much, in size, strength, or amount.

dozen   A group of twelve.

E

eagerness   Wanting something very much; strong interest: *In her eagerness to catch the bus, she tripped.*

editor   A person who chooses, revises, or checks the material that goes into a book, newspaper, or magazine.

electricity   A form of energy: *Be sure to cut off the electricity by pulling the plug before you clean the toaster.*

embarrassing   Causing an uneasy feeling: *I made an embarrassing spelling mistake.*

emperor   A person who rules a group of countries.

enormous   Very large; huge.

entire   Having no part missing; complete.

entreat   To beg: *I entreat you to help me.*

escape   To break loose; get free.

especially   In a special way; more than usually; very: *You've been especially nice to us.*

evidence   Facts or signs that help one form an opinion: *The new evidence made the detective change his mind.*

exercise   **1.** Movement of the body to keep it fit: *My daily exercises keep my body feeling good.* **2.** To move the body to keep it fit: *I exercise every day.*

extinct   Having died out: *Some kinds of birds have become extinct.*

F

faithfully   **1.** In a loyal way. **2.** Exactly: *We followed every direction faithfully.*

farewell   Good-by: *We had a farewell party for our friends.*

feather   One of the light special parts that grow from the skin of birds.

G

fleet   A large group of ships, cars, or trucks traveling together.

flock   A group of one kind of animal that lives, travels, or feeds together: *A flock of sheep was in the field.*

fool   To trick or mislead: *You fooled me into believing the story.*

forth   Forward or onward: *A swing moves back and forth.*

fortune   Luck: *I had the good fortune to meet many nice people.*

forward   Ahead; toward the future: *I am looking forward to vacation.*

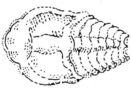

fossil   All that is left of a plant or animal that lived long ago.

frown   To wrinkle the forehead when thinking or unhappy.

future   The time that is yet to come: *We're making plans for the future.*

gallop   To run fast: *The horse galloped across the plain.*

gander   A male goose.

gaze   To look with wonder; stare: *I gazed out the window at the bright blue sky.*

gift   Something given; a present.

glacier   A large mass of ice that moves very slowly.

glum   Sad and silent.

gnaw   To bite or chew over and over: *The beaver gnawed at the trunk of the tree.*

gosling   A young goose.

gradually   Little by little; happening slowly.

grant   To give or allow: *The teacher granted the students one favor.*

greedy   Wanting more than enough: *The farmer was greedy for more land than he could use.*

grouch   A person who is always cross and complaining.

grumble To complain in a low, unhappy voice.

H

halt A stop: *The cars came to a halt when the light turned red.*

handkerchief A small piece of cloth; usually used to wipe the nose or face.

hay fever A sickness caused by the pollen of certain plants: *People with hay fever sneeze and have crying, itching eyes.*

hibernation Spending the winter asleep in a protected place: *Bears spend many months in hibernation.*

hooves A form of the word *hoof.* The tough, horny feet of some animals: *Horses, cattle, deer, and pigs have hooves.*

horrify Terrify; frighten: *I was horrified by the sight of the escaped lion.*

humble Of low importance: *We held humble jobs when we first started to work.*

I

identification The act of recognizing a particular person or thing.

identify To recognize a certain person or thing: *They could identify him by his picture.*

imitate To copy the way someone acts.

immediately Quickly; at once.

impatiently Without being calm. *We waited impatiently for the school bus.*

impossible **1.** Not able to happen or exist. **2.** Difficult to put up with: *He is impossible to be with when he is angry.*

impress To have a strong effect on the feelings or mind: *I was impressed by the artist's skill.*

Indian paintbrush A plant with bright, red leaves around small, green flowers.

instruct To give knowledge or skill to; teach.

intelligent Wise or thoughtful: *The reporter asked many intelligent questions.*

interview To speak with someone to get information.

iron A hard metal: *Iron is used to make steel.*

issue **1.** A subject that is being discussed: *School is an important issue.* **2.** A certain copy of a newspaper or magazine: *Please buy the July issue of the magazine.*

J

journey   A long trip.
judge   A person who hears and decides cases in a court of law.

L

limits   The line around an area: *We live within the city limits.*

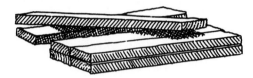

lumber   **1.** Wooden boards for building: *We used a lot of lumber to build the house.* **2.** To move or walk in a clumsy, often noisy manner: *The elephants lumbered into the circus tent.*

M

machine   A device or tool used to do work: *Special machines are used to print books.*
magnificent   Very grand and fine; large and beautiful: *We saw a magnificent palace.*
mare   A female horse.
marsh   An area of very wet land; swamp: *They looked in the marsh for toads.*

metal   A shiny, hard material that carries heat and electricity.
migration   A move from one place to another, often at a certain time of the year.

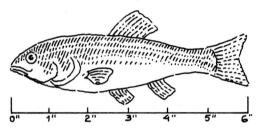

minnow   A very small fish.
mist   Many tiny drops of water: *There is a mist over the pond.*
mold   A tiny green plant that has no leaves or flowers.
monarch   **1.** A king or queen. **2.** A large black and orange butterfly.
mood   The way someone feels at a certain time: *Our coach was in a good mood after we won.*
motion   **1.** A movement of a hand, arm, or other part of the body. **2.** To move a part of the body as a signal: *The horse seemed to motion to me with its head.*
munch   To chew in a noisy, steady way: *The rabbit was munching on carrots.*
mussel   A water animal with a soft body and a pair of narrow, dark-blue shells.

mysteriously In a strange way.

mystery **1.** A story in which there is a crime or puzzling matter to solve. **2.** Something that can't be figured out.

N

natural **1.** Having to do with living things or things not made by humans: *The rocks formed a natural bridge across the stream.* **2.** Having something that is present from birth: *Lee is a natural athlete.*

noble A person of high position or title: *Many nobles came to the prince's wedding.*

nonsense Silly talk or behavior.

O

o'clock Time according to the clock: *School is out at three o'clock.*

ocean A great mass of water.

officer A member of the police force.

official Approved and accepted: *We waited for the official word about who had won the contest.*

ordinary Usual; normal: *After the flood the creek went back to its ordinary size.*

original Not copied: *We have an original painting by a famous artist.*

owe To have to pay: *How much do you owe for your lunch?*

oyster A sea animal that has a soft body and a rough, uneven shell with two parts.

P

patch **1.** A small piece of cloth used to cover a hole or tear. **2.** A small piece of land with plants growing on it: *I helped my aunt work in her vegetable patch.*

pause A short time when nothing is said or done: *There was a pause in the play when one of the actors forgot a line.*

persuade To cause someone to do or believe something by arguing, begging, or reasoning.

pillow A cloth case stuffed with a soft material, such as feathers or foam rubber.

pleasant Pleasing or agreeable.

plenty   A full amount or supply; as much of something as is needed: *I have plenty of time to catch the bus.*

plunge   To throw oneself into the water, a place, or an activity: *They plunged into the sea.*

polish   To make smooth and shiny, especially by rubbing: *I do not enjoy polishing the car.*

polite   Showing good manners.

position   The place where someone or something is found.

positive   Absolutely certain: *They had positive proof that he stole the plant.*

preserve   To keep in the same form: *The plants were preserved in perfect form.*

produce   To make or build something: *The students are producing their own newspaper.*

promptly   1. Without delay; at once: *You left promptly when John arrived.* 2. At the proper time: *I get to school promptly at 8:00 every day.*

protect   To keep from harm or danger.

prove   To show something is true: *Can you prove that the story is true?*

puzzle   To confuse: *I was puzzled by her behavior.*

Q

quarrel   An angry argument: *The twins had a quarrel over the new toy.*

quarry   A deep, open place where stone is taken out by cutting or blasting.

quench   1. To put out a fire: *We quenched the flames with many pails of water.* 2. To satisfy a thirst: *The cool drink quenched my thirst.*

R

radiantly   With brightness and happiness: *The contest winner smiled radiantly.*

rattlesnake   A poisonous American snake.

realize   To be aware of; understand completely: *I never realized how hard it is to build a boat.*

recipe   A set of directions for preparing food.

recognize   To know from past experience: *I recognized you by your voice.*

relax 1. To make or become less tight: *Try to relax your muscles.* 2. To rest.

relief A sense of well-being when an uncomfortable feeling goes away or when a difficult task has been completed: *I felt a sense of relief when the test was over.*

remains What is left after someone or something dies: *It is interesting to study the remains of the past.*

remarkable Special; not common or ordinary.

rescue To save from danger.

respectfully By showing high regard or honor: *I speak respectfully to my parents.*

responsibility Something a person is supposed to do: *It is my responsibility to set the table.*

reward Something given in return for an act or service.

ripe Fully grown and ready to be used as food: *The apples are ripe enough to be picked.*

roam To travel freely: *We roamed around looking for a place to eat.*

rodent An animal, such as a rat, mouse, squirrel, or beaver, with large teeth used for chewing.

rooster A male chicken that is fully grown.

route A group of places visited regularly.

royal Belonging to or serving a king or queen: *There is a party at the royal palace.*

rude Showing bad manners.

ruin To make useless: *The fire ruined our house.*

rustle To make a soft, crackling sound: *A breeze rustled the pages of the newspaper.*

S

saddle Something to sit on when horseback riding.

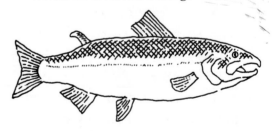

salmon A large fish that is used for food.

scarcely Barely; almost not at all: *I could scarcely find my way in the fog.*

scatter To spread or throw something about: *We scattered the chicken feed in the yard.*

scene 1. A view of a place: *The garden in bloom is a beautiful scene.* 2. A part of a play.

scientist Someone who knows a great deal about a particular part of nature.

scold To yell at or speak angrily to: *I scolded my dog after it chewed my shoes.*

scornfully In a manner that looks down on someone or something.

scrape To make a harsh sound by rubbing something on a surface: *She scraped the chalk on the blackboard.*

scurry To run or move about quickly: *The squirrel scurried up the tree with its food.*

shift To move from one place to another: *The clerk shifted the packages to the side.*

shiver To shake from cold, fear, or excitement.

shoot A plant or part of a plant that has just begun to grow.

shrill Having a high, sharp sound: *The coach uses a shrill whistle in practice.*

simply Just: *I am simply not able to go before noon.*

skeleton The connected bones of the body of an animal.

skid To slip or slide over a slippery surface: *The sled skidded on a patch of ice.*

skillet A frying pan.

sleet Frozen or almost frozen rain.

sleigh A carriage on metal runners: *Have you ever gone on a sleigh ride on a snowy day?*

slender Thin; slim.

smooth Not rough; even: *Babies have smooth skin.*

sniffling Weeping; crying: *I didn't want my friends to see me sniffling over the sad movie.*

snore To breathe loudly while sleeping.

soldier A person who serves in an army.

source Something or someone that gives information: *A glossary is a source of information.*

spirits A person's mood or state of mind: *Though he was very sick, he was in good spirits.*

splash To jump into or move through liquid: *I splashed into the water.*

splendid 1. Very beautiful: *There was a splendid sunset last evening.* 2. Excellent or fine: *What a splendid idea!*

spring **1.** A natural fountain or flow of water: *The water from the spring is very cold.* **2.** The time of year after winter.

squawk A loud, screeching sound, such as a parrot or chicken makes.

stallion A male horse that is fully grown.

stampede A sudden, violent rush of animals, such as horses, cattle, or buffalo.

state A part of a country: *Utah is a state in the United States.*

steer **1.** A young bull that is raised for food. **2.** To turn in a certain direction.

step **1.** A movement of a foot, as in walking. **2.** A flat place on which people can go up or down: *We walked up the steps.*

sternly In a firm way: *The teacher spoke sternly to the noisy class.*

stew A mixture of pieces of meat or vegetables in a liquid.

stray To wander about; get lost: *Our cat strayed away from home.*

struck A form of the word *strike*. Hit: *The ball struck the wall.*

strung A form of the word *string*. Arranged in a line.

stumble To trip and almost fall.

surround To be on all sides of; make a circle around: *Beautiful flowers surrounded the park.*

survive To stay alive through: *I hope the little tree I planted will survive the winter.*

suspect **1.** A person who is thought to have done something wrong: *The police caught a suspect.* **2.** To think something: *I suspect you are right.*

suspicion The thought that someone has done wrong: *Are you under suspicion?*

swallow To take food or liquid from the mouth into the stomach: *I swallowed a lot of water when I was swimming.*

swamp An area of soft and wet land.

sway To move back and forth or from side to side: *The trees are swaying in the wind.*

sweetly In a very pleasing way: *The little girl smiled sweetly.*

swoop To move in a quick, sweeping way: *An owl swooped down and caught a mouse.*

swung A form of the word *swing*. Moved back and forth.

T

taught A form of the word *teach*. Helped someone to learn.

tremble To shake, as from a strong blow, the cold, or a fear: *I trembled from the cold.*

trust **1.** Belief in someone or something: *I must live up to your trust.* **2.** To believe in: *I trust you.*

tune **1.** A song: *I can play a few tunes.* **2.** To put in proper sound: *I tuned my guitar.*

twig A small branch of a tree or shrub.

U

Union The United States: *The Union has fifty states.*

unsteady Shaky: *Don't climb on the unsteady ladder.*

urgent Needing quick attention: *Read the message right away, because it's urgent!*

V

vanish To disappear: *The sun vanished behind a cloud.*

W

wail To make a long, loud cry because of sadness or pain: *We heard the wild animal wail in hunger.*

wedding The ceremony of becoming married.

whip To move suddenly or quickly: *The wind whipped the leaves around.*

wild **1.** Not cared for by people. **2.** Not tame: *Wild animals live in the jungle.*

wisdom Good judgment in knowing what to do and what is good, bad, right, and wrong: *A person may gain wisdom through experience.*

wit The ability to think clearly: *You need to have a sharp wit to win at chess.*

wobble To move unsteadily from side to side: *The legs of the chair were so loose that it wobbled back and forth.*

women A form of *woman*. Female human beings.

worry To feel uneasy: *You will not have to worry about the test if you study.*

wrist The place where the arm and hand come together: *I like to wear bracelets on my wrist.*

Read
Write
Listen
Speak

Read

Here are some things to remember when you meet a new word.

1 Think about the sounds the letters stand for. Think about what the sentence is saying. Be sure the word you name makes sense in the sentence.

- When a word begins with the syllable *a, be, re,* or *ex*, think about the sounds those letters stand for in *around, beside, remember,* and *except.*
- When a word ends with the syllable *ful, ly, ty, tion, less, ness,* or *ment*, think about the sounds those letters stand for in *helpful, slowly, sixty, station, helpless, kindness,* and *apartment.*

2 A word may seem new. But you may already know its parts.

- Look for a word to which one or more endings and syllables have been added. Remember that its spelling may have changed.

  We were **hoping** for a nice **sunny** day.
  (hope + -ing, sun + -y)

- Look for small words that have been put together to make a compound word.

  We will go **downtown** to shop.
  My bed has a wooden **headboard.**

③ Some words that you already know have more than one meaning. Use the other words in the sentence to help you find the meaning that makes sense.

School begins in the **fall.**
(**fall** – "a season of the year")

We watched an apple **fall** from the tree.
(**fall** – "to drop")

④ If you do not know what a word means, look it up in a glossary or a dictionary.

Reading Stories

When you read a story, you read for fun. You read to find out about the people and events in the story. You want to understand the story. Use these ideas to understand and remember the stories you read.

Before You Read

❶ Read the title, and look at the pictures.
- What do the title and pictures tell you?
- Can you tell what the story will be about?
- What do you already know about the topic?

❷ Read the author's name.
- Have you read any other stories by this author? What were those stories about?

❸ Think about the kinds of things you want to find out in a story.
- Who are the main characters?
- When and where does the story take place?
- What are the main events in the story?

While You Read

❶ Remember the most important events.

❷ Try to predict what might happen next.

❸ Read to see if your predictions are correct.

❹ Ask questions about the story.
- Does the story make sense to you?
- Are there any parts you don't understand?

❺ Read story parts again if they are not clear.

OLD BLUE
by Sibyl Hancock

Old Blue, the lead steer, is leading other longhorn cattle across the trail. Something happens during a storm. Davy has an idea. How will his idea help?

254

After You Read

❶ Think about what happened in the story.
- What were the most important events that took place? Why did they happen?

❷ Decide how the story made you feel.
- Did you enjoy the story? Why or why not?
- Who was your favorite character in the story? Why? Was there someone you didn't like? Why?
- Would you like to read other stories by this author? Why or why not?

➡

3 **Compare the events in the story to events in your own life.**

- Did something that happened to a story character ever happen to you? What did you do?

4 **Think about other stories you have read.**

- How was this story like others you have read? How was it different?

Reading to Learn

When you read textbooks and articles, you are reading to learn. Use these ideas to understand and remember the information you read.

Before You Read

1 **Take a quick look at what you are going to read.**

- Read the title and headings.
- Look at the pictures. Read any captions.

2 **Think about the topic.**

- What do you already know about the topic?
- What do you think you will find out about it?

While You Read

❶ Think about what you are learning.
- Read slowly and carefully.
- Find important information to remember about the topic.
- Make sure you understand the meanings of any important words or terms.

❷ Ask yourself questions about the information you are learning.

❸ Make sure you understand what you are reading.
- Check yourself by going back and reading again the parts that are not clear to you.

Leaving Winter Behind

Winter is a hard time for birds in the north. They do not mind the cold weather because their feathers keep them warm. However, they do have a hard time getting enough to eat because the ground is often frozen.

Many birds cannot find enough food in winter. When the days grow shorter, they fly south. In the south, food is easy to find.

Bull moose in woods foraging for food

Moose, the largest members of the deer family, also spend the winter in herds. They travel together through swamps and woods, where they can be protected from strong winds. They feed on twigs and young shoots of trees. The moose's long legs help them walk easily in deep snow.

Geese making their journey south in V formation

197

After You Read

❶ Think about the information you have learned.
- What was the topic?
- What important facts did you learn about this topic? Did you learn some important words or terms?

❷ Answer the questions you asked while you were reading.

❸ Think about the topic.
- Did you like what you read? What else do you want to learn about this topic?

Write

The Writing Process

➊ Prewriting

Before you begin to write, decide what you want to write about. Here is one way to choose a topic.

- Make a list of ideas.
- Think about each idea on your list.
    Do you know enough to write about the idea?
    Is there too much to tell?
    Would your readers be interested in the idea?
- Decide which idea is best to write about.
- Circle the idea. It will be your topic.

Rocky Point Beach

haunted house

my dog Pinto

Winnie's aunt wanted a display for her office wall. She asked Winnie to write and draw something. Winnie decided to write a description and draw a picture to go with it. She made a list of ideas. She thought about each one. Then she circled the best idea.

After you pick your topic, make a plan. Here are some things to do to plan the writing of a description.

- Write a sentence about your topic that will make your readers want to find out more.
- Make a cluster. Write your topic in the center. Write details around your topic. Use words that tell how your topic looks and feels. Describe any sounds, smells, and tastes. Draw lines to connect ideas.

Here is Winnie's plan.

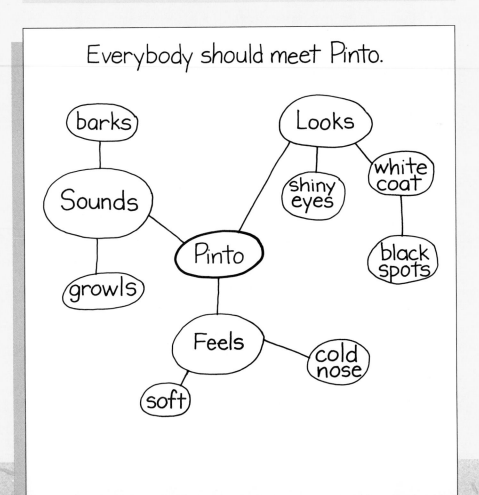

❷ Write a First Draft

After you have a plan, write a first draft. A first draft is a first try. Do not worry about mistakes. Leave plenty of room to make changes later.

Here are some things to think about as you write a description.

- Look at your plan as you write.
- Start with the opening sentence you have written.
- In your other sentences, use describing words from your cluster.

Here is Winnie's first draft.

Everybody should meet Pinto.
He has a white coat and black
spots on it his eyes are shiny.
~~His coat~~ He feels soft. He has a
cold nose. He growl and bark
and proten to be big and
scarry. Can you tell what
Pinto is ?

❸ Revise

When you revise, look at your writing to change it. Different kinds of writing may need different kinds of changes. Here are some ways to revise a description.

- Read your description to yourself.

  Does your first sentence tell about the topic in an interesting way?

  Did you describe how something looked?

  Did you include details about other senses?

  Did you tell just enough?

- Change words to make your description clearer.
- Read your description to a listener. Think about what your listener asks or suggests.
- Revise your description so that your readers can picture your topic clearly.

Winnie read her description to her friend Sam. Sam listened carefully.

Sam: I liked the riddle at the end.

Winnie: Are there any details I should add?

Sam: Does Pinto pretend to be big because he is really little?

Winnie: Yes, he's small. I'll add that. Thanks.

Winnie added some describing words. She changed other words. She thought about what Sam had said. She revised her description. Here is part of Winnie's revised draft.

Everybody should meet Pinto.
He has a white coat and black
soft   with
His fur is short.
spots on it his eyes are shiny.
brown and
His coat He feels soft. He has a
cold nose. He growl and bark
black   but he is just
and proten to be big and
He really is small and gentel.
scarry. Can you tell what
Pinto is ?

4 Proofread

Slowly read again what you have written, word by word. Check for mistakes, and fix them.

- Use the proofreading checklist and marks to fix your revised draft.

Proofreading Checklist

Did I

☑ 1. use complete sentences?

☑ 2. use capital letters and end marks correctly?

☑ 3. use other punctuation marks correctly?

☑ 4. indent each paragraph?

☑ 5. spell every word correctly?

Proofreading Marks

¶ Indent a paragraph.

∧ Add something.

⌐ Take out something.

≡ Capitalize.

/ Make a small letter.

— Fix spelling.

Here is Winnie's proofread description.

Everybody should meet Pinto.
He has a <u>soft</u> white coat <s>and</s> <u>with</u> black
spots. <s>on it</s> <u>His fur is short.</u> his eyes are <u>brown and</u> shiny.
<s>His coat</s> He feels soft. He has a
cold <u>black</u> nose. He growls and barks <u>but he is just</u>
and <s>proten</s> <u>pretending</u> to be big and <u>gentle</u>
<s>scarry.</s> <u>scary</u> <u>He really is small and gentel.</u> Can you tell what
Pinto is ?

393

⑤ Publish

When you are ready to share what you have written, make a final copy.

- Copy your revised draft in your best handwriting.
- Proofread once again. Fix any mistakes.
- Think of a special way to share your work.

Winnie made a drawing of Pinto to go with her description. She delivered them to Aunt Vicki's office.

Listen and Speak

Listening

When you listen, think about your purpose
for listening.

1 Listening to a story for enjoyment
- Listen for important events.
- Think about how each event leads to another.
- Try to picture the people and places.

2 Listening to a lesson or report for information
- Think about the topic.
- Listen for details about the topic.
- Listen for important new words.
- Think of questions to ask about the topic.

3 Listening for directions
- Listen for each step. Think about the order of steps.
- Try to picture each step.
- Listen for words that describe actions.
- Ask questions if you do not understand each step.

Speaking

When you give a talk or read aloud, you want your listeners to learn information or to enjoy a story.

❶ Giving a talk

- Choose a topic that will interest your listeners.
- Plan what you will say about the topic.
- Look at your listeners as you speak.
- Speak loudly and clearly.

❷ Reading aloud

- Read silently first. Then practice reading aloud to yourself until you are reading smoothly.
- Read loudly enough for all to hear.
- Say your words clearly.
- Hold your head up so that your listeners can see your face. Hold your book down so that it does not block your voice.
- Look at your listeners as often as you can.
- Think about the meaning of what you are reading. Try to make your voice sound the way the author or the characters might sound.

Discussing Writing

When you are getting ready to revise something you have written, read it aloud to a friend. You and your listener can discuss the writing to make it better.

1 A writer may ask these questions.
- Was my beginning interesting?
- Was anything not clear?
- Are there any details I should add?

2 A listener should follow these guides.
- Listen carefully as the writer reads.
- Tell something you liked about the writing.
- Ask questions about anything you did not understand.
- Make suggestions if the writer asks for help.
- Be polite.

Credits

Teason **94–95** Stella Ormai **96–119** Rosekranz Hoffman **122–123** Jamichael Henterly **126–142** Michael Codd **143** Kari Emmons **144–149** Donna Diamond **170–171** Jamichael Henterly **172–173** James Marshall **174–185** Jeremy Guitar **186–189** Donna Diamond **200–213** Patrick Kernan **215–233** (illustrations) Nick Harris (borders) © Faith Harrison **236–237** Jamichael Henterly **240–272** Collette Slade **274–279** Donna Diamond **280–291** Paul Breeden **294–307** Eric Ingraham **308–313** Donna Diamond **314–331** Sally Schaedler **332–333** David Kelly **342–343** Donna Diamond **346–367** Haru Wells **368–380** George M. Ulrich **382–397** Linda Phinney **389, 390, 392, 393** Mary Keefe **25, 29, 79, 213, 263** Meg Kelleher

Photographers: (bottom left, top right) © David Muench Photography **61** (bottom right) © Ken Sakamoto/Black Star **84–88** Chuck Shaft **89** © Mark Sherman/Bruce Coleman, Inc. **90** © Dr. E. R. Degginger **91** © Norman O. Tomalin/Bruce Coleman Inc. **92** © Dr. E. R. Degginger **148** Michal Heron **188, 189** (top) © Dr. E. R. Degginger **189** (bottom) Mrs. Dorothy S. Long/ Photo/Nats **190** © John Shaw/Bruce Coleman Inc. **191** © Wayne Lankinen/Bruce Coleman Inc. **192** (left) © Wolfgang Bayer **192** (right) © Harry Engels/Bruce Coleman Inc. **193** (bottom) © Joe & Carol McDonald/Animals Animals **194** © C. C. Lockwood/Bruce Coleman Inc. **195** (right) John Dommers/Photo Researchers, Inc. **195** (left) **196** (top, middle) © Leonard Lee Rue III/Bruce Coleman Inc. **196** (bottom) © Marty Stouffer/ Animals Animals **197** (top, bottom) © W. K. Almond/Stock Boston **197** (bottom) Grant Heilman Photography **198** (top) Stephen J. Krasemann/Peter Arnold, Inc. **198** (middle) © Martin W. Grosnick/Bruce Coleman Inc. **198** (bottom) © Harry N. Darrow/Bruce Coleman Inc. **199** © Peter Menzel **230** © Dr. E. R. Degginger **249** Alaska Historical Library **273** Grant Heilman Photography **274** (left) © T. Vander Schmidt/Animals Animals **274** (middle) © Millard H. Sharp/Click/Chicago **274** (right) © Tom J. Ulrich/Click/Chicago **277** Suen-o Lindblad/ Photo Researchers, Inc. **292–293** © David Muench Photography **334–341** Mark Halevi **340** (bottom) © Susan Lapides **382** Nancy Sheehan **388, 391, 394, 397** Michal Heron